SUNNY the SKIN SHIELD

DEDICATION

To my sons-

You are the reason behind every page, every word, and every dream brought to life in this story. You are my heart, my inspiration, and the reason these stories came to life. Watching you grow, learn, and shine brighter each day is my greatest joy. This book - and the series to come - begins with you and was written with love that will last far beyond these pages.

To every child-

May this story be a reminder that you are strong, bright, and protected. This is just the beginning of a series made to help you grow with confidence, curiosity, and courage wherever life takes you.

Ryu loved to play outside in the warm, sunny air.
He ran, climbed, and laughed all day long.

His big brother, Dash, was always right beside him.
They were the best adventure team.

One morning Ryu said, "Do I have to wear sunscreen?"
He made a little scrunchy face.

Dash laughed and said, "You don't want to get burned!"
"Trust me I've learned the hard way."

That night, Ryu had a dream about his skin.
It looked like a strong, shiny castle.

Suddenly, ZAP! Bright sun rays came zooming down!
"Oh no!" Ryu shouted.

Then a glowing friend appeared.
"I'm Sunny the Shield! I protect your skin!"

Sunny covered the castle like a soft, shiny blanket.
The sun rays bounced right off, BOING!

"They can't get us?" Ryu asked.
"Not if you put sunscreen on every day!" Sunny said.

Ryu woke up with a big smile.
"Dash! We need sunscreen!"

The brothers put sunscreen on their faces, arms, and legs.
"We're protecting our castles!" they cheered.

Now Ryu and Dash wear sunscreen before every adventure.

PARENT PRO TIP
Find a Sunscreen with Zinc Oxide & Titanium Dioxide
ZINC OXIDE
TITANIUM DIOXIDE
HARMFUL UV RAYS
SUNSCREEN LAYER
SKIN SURFACE
SKIN CELLS
DEEPER SKIN LAYERS
They sit on top of the skin and block harmful rays like a tiny shield.
Sunscreen should go on 15 minutes before sun exposure not right as you walk out the door.
Kids need more sunscreen than you think, about a full shot glass amount to cover the whole body.
"Waterproof" sunscreen isn't real. Look for water resistant and always reapply after swimming.
OCT 26
Sunscreen expires! Check the date. Old sunscreen can lose effectiveness.
Sprays are convenient, but lotions protect more evenly. (If using sprays rub them in after applying.)
LIP BALM SPF
Lips burn too – use a lip balm with SPF.
Most parents forget the sun is strongest between 10am-4pm even in cooler weather.
SUNSCREEN SPF 50+
Protecting skin early is one of the easiest ways to prevent long term damage. Little steps now,
BIG PROTECTION FOR LIFE

Pack Your Sun Safety Bag

Draw a line or circle to what belongs in your beach bag.

Sun Safety Word Search

Can you find all the hidden sun safety words?

HAT

SUN

SKIN

SAFE

Y	U	N	Y	Y	V	O	F	O	G
S	U	N	N	Y	A	S	I	N	E
U	H	A	T	E	R	A	C	S	
N	O	I	D	H	E	F	B	P	
V	S	H	A	D	E	R	F		
W	K	T	T	R	O	H	A		
S	I	I	W	A	T	E	R		
S	N	N	Y	S	S	E	E		

SUNNY

WATER

SPF

SHADE

Draw Yourself Having Fun in the Sun!

Can you draw yourself enjoying a sunny day?
Don’t forget your sun safety gear!

Sun Safety Scavenger Hunt!

Look carefully! Find and circle each item below.

Sun	Shady tree	Hat
Sunglasses	Water bottle	Sunscreen

Color Sunny the Skin Shield!

Help Sunny Get to the Soccer Field

Connect the Dots!

Follow the numbers and discover WHAT THE SURPRISE IS

Match the Colors!

Can you match each color to the correct objects?

Circle the Things That Start with "S"

Can you find everything that begins with the letter S ?

Color by Numbers

Share your sunscreen with your buddy and color the picture with the relevant colors

Sun Safety

Write the correct words on the lines

1. Always wear a __________  when you are in the sun.

2. __________  will help to protect your eyes from harmful rays of the sun.

3. Apply plenty of __________  to protect your skin from harmful rays.

4. After a few __________ 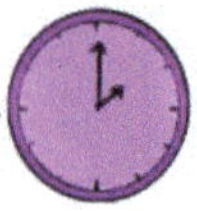 you need to reapply.

5. Cover your skin with a __________  if you can.

6. Play in the __________  for even better protection from the sun.

shade	hat	hours	sunscreen	shirt	sunglasses

ABOUT THE AUTHOR

Sierra Jeffress is a creative storyteller with a passion for bringing imagination to life through meaningful, engaging narratives. With a background in aesthetics and plastic surgery industry, she blends science, care, and creativity into everything she does.

Inspired by her love for children and storytelling, Sierra writes books that spark curiosity, build confidence, and make learning fun. Her work focuses on turning everyday lessons - like sun safety - into magical, memorable adventures.

When she's not writing, Sierra enjoys spending time with her family, working in the world of advanced skincare and laser treatments, and creating content that educates and inspires others.

ABOUT THE ILLUSTRATOR

Farheen Fatima is a Canadian children's book illustrator who brings warmth, imagination, and charm to every page she creates. With a playful illustration style and a keen eye for detail, she transforms stories into engaging visual experiences that captivate young readers.

Passionate about visual storytelling, Farheen loves collaborating with authors and publishers to bring new tales to life through her artwork.

Ready to bring your story to life? Get in touch to discuss your project and create something children will treasure for years to come.

www.littlefolkstories.com

design@littlefolkstories.com

Scan to contact

www.ingramcontent.com/pod-product-compliance
Lightning Source LLC
LaVergne TN
LVHW071535210926
848349LV00013B/136

DEDICATION

To my sons-
You are the reason behind every page, every word, and every dream brought to life in this story. You are my heart, my inspiration, and the reason these stories came to life. Watching you grow, learn, and shine brighter each day is my greatest joy. This book - and the series to come - begins with you and was written with love that will last far beyond these pages.

To every child-
May this story be a reminder that you are strong, bright, and protected. This is just the beginning of a series made to help you grow with confidence, curiosity, and courage wherever life takes you.

Ryu loved to play outside in the warm, sunny air.
He ran, climbed, and laughed all day long.

His big brother, Dash, was always right beside him.
They were the best adventure team.

One morning Ryu said, "Do I have to wear sunscreen?"
He made a little scrunchy face.

Dash laughed and said, "You don't want to get burned!"
"Trust me I've learned the hard way."

That night, Ryu had a dream about his skin.
It looked like a strong, shiny castle.

Suddenly, ZAP! Bright sun rays came zooming down!
"Oh no!" Ryu shouted.

Then a glowing friend appeared.
"I'm Sunny the Shield! I protect your skin!"

Sunny covered the castle like a soft, shiny blanket.
The sun rays bounced right off, BOING!

"They can't get us?" Ryu asked.
"Not if you put sunscreen on every day!" Sunny said.

Ryu woke up with a big smile.
"Dash! We need sunscreen!"

The brothers put sunscreen on their faces, arms, and legs. "We're protecting our castles!" they cheered.

Now Ryu and Dash wear sunscreen before every adventure.

PARENT PRO TIP
Find a Sunscreen with
Zinc Oxide & Titanium Dioxide
ZINC OXIDE
TITANIUM DIOXIDE
HARMFUL UV RAYS
SUNSCREEN LAYER
SKIN SURFACE
SKIN CELLS
DEEPER SKIN LAYERS
They sit on top of the skin and block harmful rays like a tiny shield.
Sunscreen should go on 15 minutes before sun exposure not right as you walk out the door.
Kids need more sunscreen than you think, about a full shot glass amount to cover the whole body.
"Waterproof" sunscreen isn't real. Look for water resistant and always reapply after swimming.
OCT 26
Sunscreen expires! Check the date. Old sunscreen can lose effectiveness.
Sprays are convenient, but lotions protect more evenly. (If using sprays rub them in after applying.)
LIP BALM SPF
Lips burn too – use a lip balm with SPF.
Most parents forget the sun is strongest between 10am-4pm even in cooler weather.
SUNSCREEN SPF 50+
Protecting skin early is one of the easiest ways to prevent long term damage. Little steps now,
BIG PROTECTION FOR LIFE

Pack Your Sun Safety Bag

Draw a line or circle to what belongs in your beach bag.

Sun Safety Word Search

Can you find all the hidden sun safety words?

HAT
SUN
SKIN
SAFE
SUNNY
WATER
SHADE
SPF

Y U N Y Y V O F O G
S U N N Y A S I N E
U H A T E R A C S
N O I D H E F B P
V S H A D E R F
W K T T R O H A
S I I W A T E R
S N N Y S S E E

Draw Yourself Having Fun in the Sun!

Can you draw yourself enjoying a sunny day? Don't forget your sun safety gear!

Sun Safety Scavenger Hunt!

Look carefully! Find and circle each item below.

Sun	Shady tree	Hat
Sunglasses	Water bottle	Sunscreen

Color Sunny the Skin Shield!

Help Sunny Get to the Soccer Field

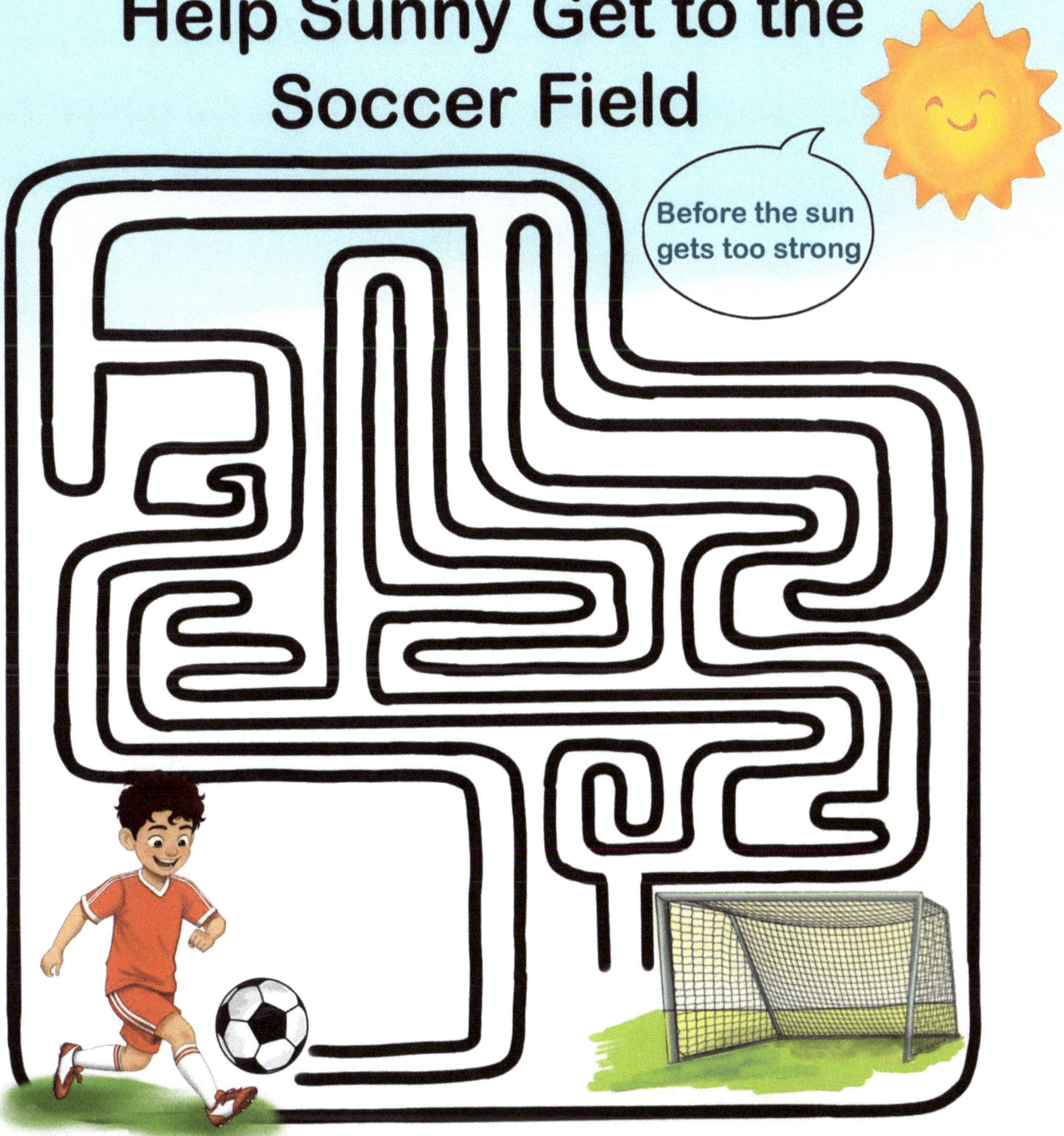

Connect the Dots!

Follow the numbers and discover WHAT THE SURPRISE IS

Match the Colors!

Can you match each color to the correct objects?

Circle the Things That Start with "S"

Can you find everything that begins with the letter S ?

Color by Numbers

Share your sunscreen with your buddy and color the picture with the relevant colors

Sun Safety

Write the correct words on the lines

1. Always wear a __________  when you are in the sun.

2. __________ 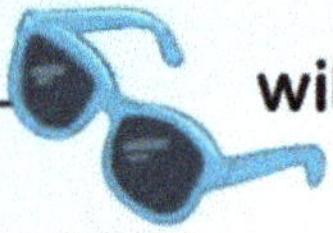 will help to protect your eyes from harmful rays of the sun.

3. Apply plenty of __________  to protect your skin from harmful rays.

4. After a few __________  you need to reapply.

5. Cover your skin with a __________  if you can.

6. Play in the __________  for even better protection from the sun.

shade	hat	hours	sunscreen	shirt	sunglasses

ABOUT THE AUTHOR

Sierra Jeffress is a creative storyteller with a passion for bringing imagination to life through meaningful, engaging narratives. With a background in aesthetics and plastic surgery industry, she blends science, care, and creativity into everything she does.

Inspired by her love for children and storytelling, Sierra writes books that spark curiosity, build confidence, and make learning fun. Her work focuses on turning everyday lessons - like sun safety - into magical, memorable adventures.

When she's not writing, Sierra enjoys spending time with her family, working in the world of advanced skincare and laser treatments, and creating content that educates and inspires others.

ABOUT THE ILLUSTRATOR

Farheen Fatima is a Canadian children's book illustrator who brings warmth, imagination, and charm to every page she creates. With a playful illustration style and a keen eye for detail, she transforms stories into engaging visual experiences that captivate young readers.

Passionate about visual storytelling, Farheen loves collaborating with authors and publishers to bring new tales to life through her artwork.

Ready to bring your story to life? Get in touch to discuss your project and create something children will treasure for years to come.

www.littlefolkstories.com

design@littlefolkstories.com

Scan to contact

www.ingramcontent.com/pod-product-compliance
Lightning Source LLC
LaVergne TN
LVHW071535210926
848349LV00013B/136

DEDICATION

To my sons-

You are the reason behind every page, every word, and every dream brought to life in this story. You are my heart, my inspiration, and the reason these stories came to life. Watching you grow, learn, and shine brighter each day is my greatest joy. This book - and the series to come - begins with you and was written with love that will last far beyond these pages.

To every child-

May this story be a reminder that you are strong, bright, and protected. This is just the beginning of a series made to help you grow with confidence, curiosity, and courage wherever life takes you.

Ryu loved to play outside in the warm, sunny air.
He ran, climbed, and laughed all day long.

His big brother, Dash, was always right beside him.
They were the best adventure team.

One morning Ryu said, "Do I have to wear sunscreen?"
He made a little scrunchy face.

Dash laughed and said, "You don't want to get burned!"
"Trust me I've learned the hard way."

That night, Ryu had a dream about his skin.
It looked like a strong, shiny castle.

Suddenly, ZAP! Bright sun rays came zooming down!
"Oh no!" Ryu shouted.

Then a glowing friend appeared.
"I'm Sunny the Shield! I protect your skin!"

Sunny covered the castle like a soft, shiny blanket.
The sun rays bounced right off, BOING!

"They can't get us?" Ryu asked.
"Not if you put sunscreen on every day!" Sunny said.

Ryu woke up with a big smile.
"Dash! We need sunscreen!"

The brothers put sunscreen on their faces, arms, and legs. "We're protecting our castles!" they cheered.

Now Ryu and Dash wear sunscreen before every adventure.

PARENT PRO TIP

Find a Sunscreen with Zinc Oxide & Titanium Dioxide

- Sunscreen should go on 15 minutes before sun exposure not right as you walk out the door.
- Kids need more sunscreen than you think, about a full shot glass amount to cover the whole body.
- "Waterproof" sunscreen isn't real. Look for water resistant and always reapply after swimming.
- Sunscreen expires! Check the date. Old sunscreen can lose effectiveness.
- Sprays are convenient, but lotions protect more evenly. (if using sprays rub them in after applying.)
- Lips burn too – use a lip balm with SPF.
- Most parents forget the sun is strongest between 10am-4pm even in cooler weather.

Protecting skin early is one of the easiest ways to prevent long term damage. Little steps now,

BIG PROTECTION FOR LIFE

Pack Your Sun Safety Bag

Draw a line or circle to what belongs in your beach bag.

Sun Safety Word Search

Can you find all the hidden sun safety words?

Y U N Y Y V O F O G
S U N N Y A S I N E
U H A T E R A C S
N O I D H E F B P
V S H A D E R F
W K T T R O H A
S I I W A T E R
S N N Y S S E E

SUN
SKIN
SUNNY
SPF
HAT
SAFE
WATER
SHADE

Draw Yourself Having Fun in the Sun!

Can you draw yourself enjoying a sunny day?
Don't forget your sun safety gear!

Sun Safety Scavenger Hunt!

Look carefully! Find and circle each item below.

Sun	Shady tree	Hat
Sunglasses	Water bottle	Sunscreen

Color Sunny the Skin Shield!

Help Sunny Get to the Soccer Field

Connect the Dots!

Follow the numbers and discover WHAT THE SURPRISE IS

Match the Colors!

Can you match each color to the correct objects?

Circle the Things That Start with “S”

Can you find everything that begins with the letter S ?

Color by Numbers

Share your sunscreen with your buddy and color the picture with the relevant colors

1 2 3 4 5 6 7 8 9

Sun Safety 

Write the correct words on the lines

1. Always wear a __________  when you are in the sun.

2. __________ 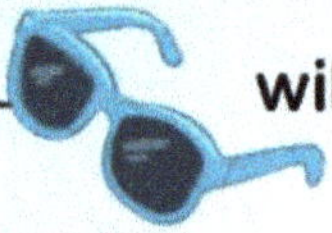 will help to protect your eyes from harmful rays of the sun.

3. Apply plenty of __________  to protect your skin from harmful rays.

4. After a few __________  you need to reapply.

5. Cover your skin with a __________ 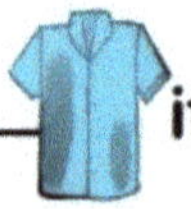 if you can.

6. Play in the __________  for even better protection from the sun.

shade	hat	hours	sunscreen	shirt	sunglasses

ABOUT THE AUTHOR

Sierra Jeffress is a creative storyteller with a passion for bringing imagination to life through meaningful, engaging narratives. With a background in aesthetics and plastic surgery industry, she blends science, care, and creativity into everything she does.

Inspired by her love for children and storytelling, Sierra writes books that spark curiosity, build confidence, and make learning fun. Her work focuses on turning everyday lessons - like sun safety - into magical, memorable adventures.

When she's not writing, Sierra enjoys spending time with her family, working in the world of advanced skincare and laser treatments, and creating content that educates and inspires others.

ABOUT THE ILLUSTRATOR

Farheen Fatima is a Canadian children's book illustrator who brings warmth, imagination, and charm to every page she creates. With a playful illustration style and a keen eye for detail, she transforms stories into engaging visual experiences that captivate young readers.

Passionate about visual storytelling, Farheen loves collaborating with authors and publishers to bring new tales to life through her artwork.

Ready to bring your story to life? Get in touch to discuss your project and create something children will treasure for years to come.

www.littlefolkstories.com

design@littlefolkstories.com

Scan to contact

www.ingramcontent.com/pod-product-compliance
Lightning Source LLC
LaVergne TN
LVHW071535210926
848349LV00013B/136

DEDICATION

To my sons-

You are the reason behind every page, every word, and every dream brought to life in this story. You are my heart, my inspiration, and the reason these stories came to life. Watching you grow, learn, and shine brighter each day is my greatest joy. This book - and the series to come - begins with you and was written with love that will last far beyond these pages.

To every child-

May this story be a reminder that you are strong, bright, and protected. This is just the beginning of a series made to help you grow with confidence, curiosity, and courage wherever life takes you.

Ryu loved to play outside in the warm, sunny air.
He ran, climbed, and laughed all day long.

His big brother, Dash, was always right beside him.
They were the best adventure team.

One morning Ryu said, "Do I have to wear sunscreen?"
He made a little scrunchy face.

Dash laughed and said, "You don't want to get burned!"
"Trust me I've learned the hard way."

That night, Ryu had a dream about his skin.
It looked like a strong, shiny castle.

Suddenly, ZAP! Bright sun rays came zooming down!
"Oh no!" Ryu shouted.

Then a glowing friend appeared.
"I'm Sunny the Shield! I protect your skin!"

Sunny covered the castle like a soft, shiny blanket.
The sun rays bounced right off, BOING!

"They can't get us?" Ryu asked.
"Not if you put sunscreen on every day!" Sunny said.

Ryu woke up with a big smile.
"Dash! We need sunscreen!"

The brothers put sunscreen on their faces, arms, and legs.
"We're protecting our castles!" they cheered.

Now Ryu and Dash wear sunscreen before every adventure.

PARENT PRO TIP
Find a Sunscreen with
Zinc Oxide & Titanium Dioxide
ZINC OXIDE
TITANIUM DIOXIDE
HARMFUL UV RAYS
SUNSCREEN LAYER
SKIN SURFACE
SKIN CELLS
DEEPER SKIN LAYERS
They sit on top of the skin and block harmful rays like a tiny shield.
Sunscreen should go on 15 minutes before sun exposure not right as you walk out the door.
Kids need more sunscreen than you think, about a full shot glass amount to cover the whole body.
"Waterproof" sunscreen isn't real. Look for water resistant and always reapply after swimming.
OCT 26
Sunscreen expires! Check the date. Old sunscreen can lose effectiveness.
Sprays are convenient, but lotions protect more evenly. (If using sprays rub them in after applying.)
LIP BALM SPF
Lips burn too – use a lip balm with SPF.
Most parents forget the sun is strongest between 10am-4pm even in cooler weather.
SUNSCREEN SPF 50+
Protecting skin early is one of the easiest ways to prevent long term damage. Little steps now,
BIG PROTECTION FOR LIFE

Pack Your Sun Safety Bag

Draw a line or circle to what belongs in your beach bag.

Sun Safety Word Search

Can you find all the hidden sun safety words?

SUN

SKIN

SUNNY

SPF

HAT

SAFE

WATER

SHADE

Y U N Y Y V O F O G
S U N N Y A S I N E
U H A T E R A C S
N O I D H E F B P
V S H A D E R F
W K T T R O H A
S I I W A T E R
S N N Y S S E E

Draw Yourself Having Fun in the Sun!

Can you draw yourself enjoying a sunny day?
Don't forget your sun safety gear!

Sun Safety Scavenger Hunt!

Look carefully! Find and circle each item below.

Sun	Shady tree	Hat
Sunglasses	Water bottle	Sunscreen

Color Sunny the Skin Shield!

Help Sunny Get to the Soccer Field

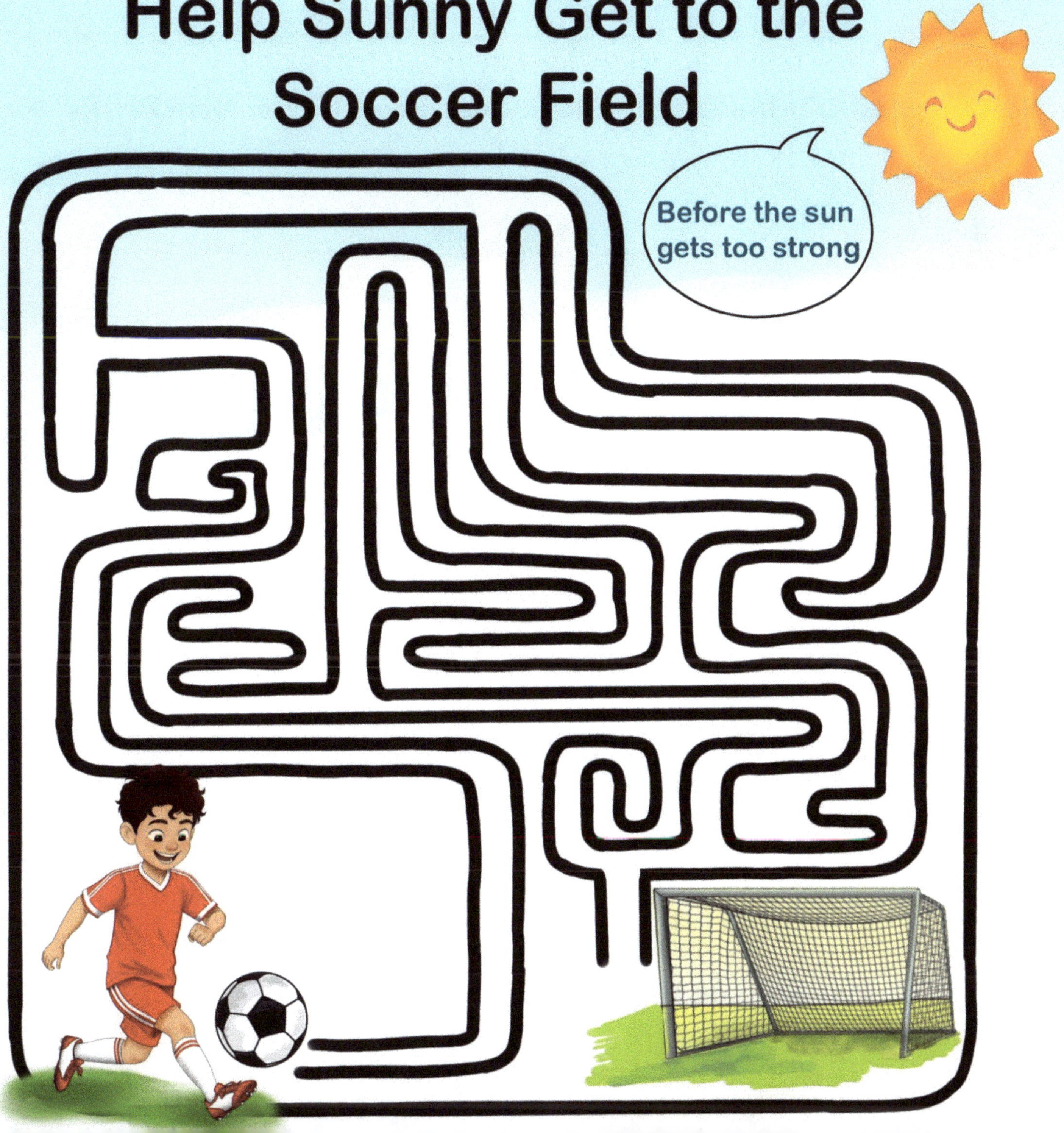

Connect the Dots!

Follow the numbers and discover WHAT THE SURPRISE IS

Match the Colors!

Can you match each color to the correct objects?

Circle the Things That Start with "S"

Can you find everything that begins with the letter S ?

Color by Numbers

Share your sunscreen with your buddy and color the picture with the relevant colors

1 2 3 4 5 6 7 8 9

Sun Safety

Write the correct words on the lines

1. Always wear a __________  when you are in the sun.

2. __________  will help to protect your eyes from harmful rays of the sun.

3. Apply plenty of __________ 

to protect your skin from harmful rays.

4. After a few __________  you need to reapply.

5. Cover your skin with a __________  if you can.

6. Play in the __________  for even better protection from the sun.

shade	hat	hours	sunscreen	shirt	sunglasses

ABOUT THE AUTHOR

Sierra Jeffress is a creative storyteller with a passion for bringing imagination to life through meaningful, engaging narratives. With a background in aesthetics and plastic surgery industry, she blends science, care, and creativity into everything she does.

Inspired by her love for children and storytelling, Sierra writes books that spark curiosity, build confidence, and make learning fun. Her work focuses on turning everyday lessons - like sun safety - into magical, memorable adventures.

When she's not writing, Sierra enjoys spending time with her family, working in the world of advanced skincare and laser treatments, and creating content that educates and inspires others.

ABOUT THE ILLUSTRATOR

Farheen Fatima is a Canadian children's book illustrator who brings warmth, imagination, and charm to every page she creates. With a playful illustration style and a keen eye for detail, she transforms stories into engaging visual experiences that captivate young readers.

Passionate about visual storytelling, Farheen loves collaborating with authors and publishers to bring new tales to life through her artwork.

Ready to bring your story to life? Get in touch to discuss your project and create something children will treasure for years to come.

www.littlefolkstories.com

design@littlefolkstories.com

Scan to contact

www.ingramcontent.com/pod-product-compliance
Lightning Source LLC
LaVergne TN
LVHW071535210926
848349LV00013B/136
* 9 7 9 8 2 3 4 1 0 3 7 5 8 *

DEDICATION

To my sons–
You are the reason behind every page, every word, and every dream brought to life in this story. You are my heart, my inspiration, and the reason these stories came to life. Watching you grow, learn, and shine brighter each day is my greatest joy. This book - and the series to come - begins with you and was written with love that will last far beyond these pages.

To every child–
May this story be a reminder that you are strong, bright, and protected. This is just the beginning of a series made to help you grow with confidence, curiosity, and courage wherever life takes you.

Ryu loved to play outside in the warm, sunny air.
He ran, climbed, and laughed all day long.

His big brother, Dash, was always right beside him.
They were the best adventure team.

One morning Ryu said, "Do I have to wear sunscreen?"
He made a little scrunchy face.

Dash laughed and said, "You don't want to get burned!"
"Trust me I've learned the hard way."

That night, Ryu had a dream about his skin.
It looked like a strong, shiny castle.

Suddenly, ZAP! Bright sun rays came zooming down!
"Oh no!" Ryu shouted.

Then a glowing friend appeared.
"I'm Sunny the Shield! I protect your skin!"

Sunny covered the castle like a soft, shiny blanket.
The sun rays bounced right off, BOING!

"They can't get us?" Ryu asked.
"Not if you put sunscreen on every day!" Sunny said.

Ryu woke up with a big smile.
"Dash! We need sunscreen!"

The brothers put sunscreen on their faces, arms, and legs.
"We're protecting our castles!" they cheered.

Now Ryu and Dash wear sunscreen before every adventure.

PARENT PRO TIP

Find a Sunscreen with Zinc Oxide & Titanium Dioxide

- Sunscreen should go on 15 minutes before sun exposure not right as you walk out the door.
- Kids need more sunscreen than you think, about a full shot glass amount to cover the whole body.
- "Waterproof" sunscreen isn't real. Look for water resistant and always reapply after swimming.
- Sunscreen expires! Check the date. Old sunscreen can lose effectiveness.
- Sprays are convenient, but lotions protect more evenly. (If using sprays rub them in after applying.)
- Lips burn too – use a lip balm with SPF.
- Most parents forget the sun is strongest between 10am-4pm even in cooler weather.

Protecting skin early is one of the easiest ways to prevent long term damage. Little steps now,

BIG PROTECTION FOR LIFE

Pack Your Sun Safety Bag

Draw a line or circle to what belongs in your beach bag.

Sun Safety Word Search

Can you find all the hidden sun safety words?

HAT

SUN

SKIN

SAFE

SUNNY

WATER

SPF

SHADE

Y U N Y Y V O F O G
S U N N Y A S I N E
U H A T E R A C S
N O I D H E F B P
V S H A D E R F
W K T T R O H A
S I I W A T E R
S N N Y S S E E

Draw Yourself Having Fun in the Sun!

Can you draw yourself enjoying a sunny day?
Don't forget your sun safety gear!

Sun Safety Scavenger Hunt!

Look carefully! Find and circle each item below.

Sun	Shady tree	Hat
Sunglasses	Water bottle	Sunscreen

Color Sunny the Skin Shield!

Help Sunny Get to the Soccer Field

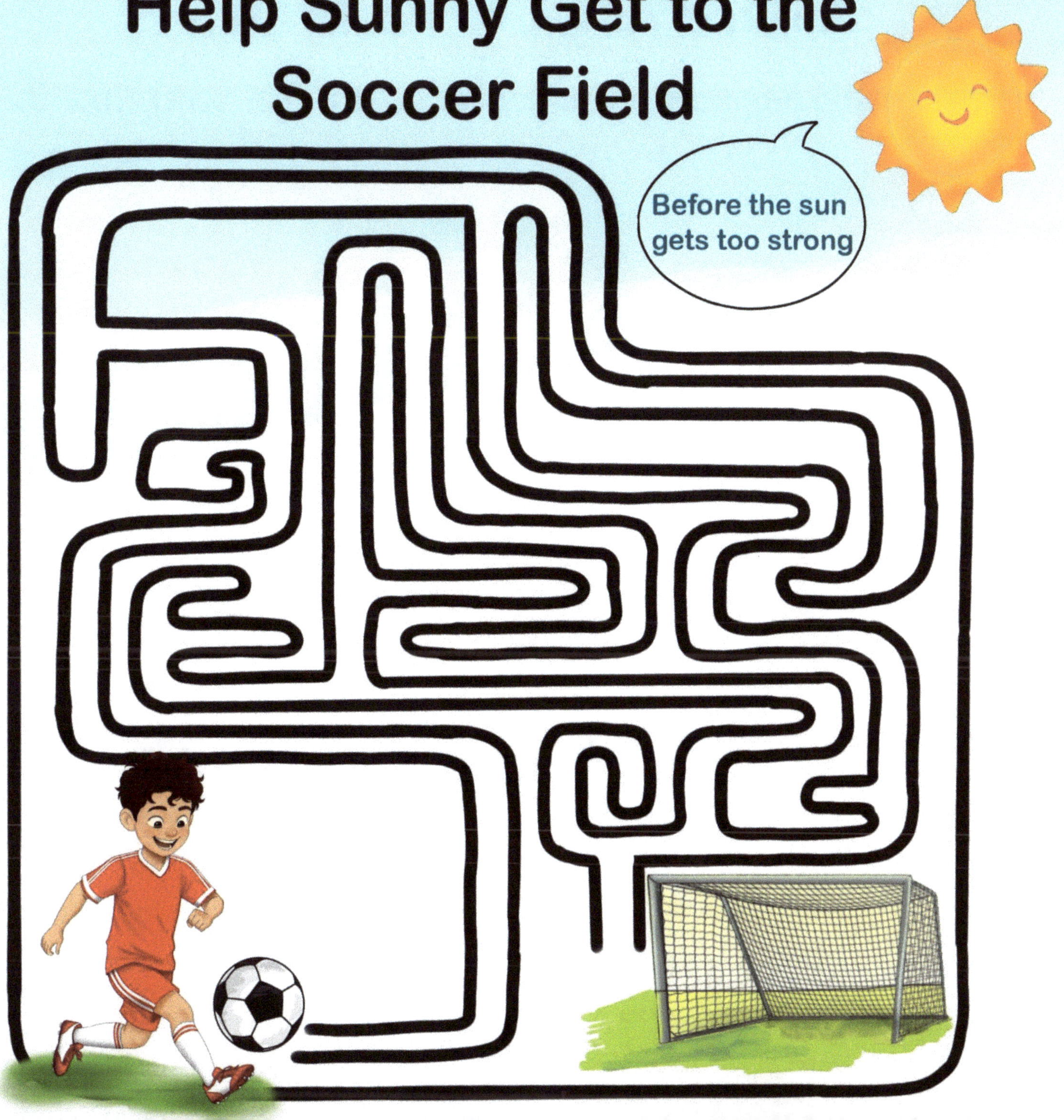

Connect the Dots!

Follow the numbers and discover WHAT THE SURPRISE IS

Match the Colors!

Can you match each color to the correct objects?

Circle the Things That Start with "S"

Can you find everything that begins with the letter S ?

Color by Numbers

Share your sunscreen with your buddy and color the picture with the relevant colors

Sun Safety

Write the correct words on the lines

1. Always wear a __________  when you are in the sun.

2. __________ 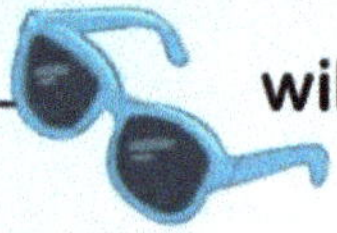 will help to protect your eyes from harmful rays of the sun.

3. Apply plenty of __________ 

to protect your skin from harmful rays.

4. After a few __________ 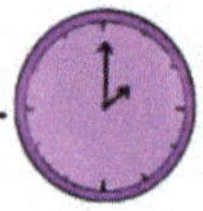 you need to reapply.

5. Cover your skin with a __________ 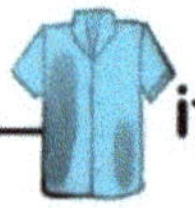 if you can.

6. Play in the __________  for even better protection from the sun.

shade	hat	hours	sunscreen	shirt	sunglasses

ABOUT THE AUTHOR

Sierra Jeffress is a creative storyteller with a passion for bringing imagination to life through meaningful, engaging narratives. With a background in aesthetics and plastic surgery industry, she blends science, care, and creativity into everything she does.

Inspired by her love for children and storytelling, Sierra writes books that spark curiosity, build confidence, and make learning fun. Her work focuses on turning everyday lessons - like sun safety - into magical, memorable adventures.

When she's not writing, Sierra enjoys spending time with her family, working in the world of advanced skincare and laser treatments, and creating content that educates and inspires others.

ABOUT THE ILLUSTRATOR

Farheen Fatima is a Canadian children's book illustrator who brings warmth, imagination, and charm to every page she creates. With a playful illustration style and a keen eye for detail, she transforms stories into engaging visual experiences that captivate young readers.

Passionate about visual storytelling, Farheen loves collaborating with authors and publishers to bring new tales to life through her artwork.

Ready to bring your story to life? Get in touch to discuss your project and create something children will treasure for years to come.

www.littlefolkstories.com

design@littlefolkstories.com

Scan to contact

www.ingramcontent.com/pod-product-compliance
Lightning Source LLC
LaVergne TN
LVHW071535210926
848349LV00013B/136

DEDICATION

To my sons-
You are the reason behind every page, every word, and every dream brought to life in this story. You are my heart, my inspiration, and the reason these stories came to life. Watching you grow, learn, and shine brighter each day is my greatest joy. This book - and the series to come - begins with you and was written with love that will last far beyond these pages.

To every child-
May this story be a reminder that you are strong, bright, and protected. This is just the beginning of a series made to help you grow with confidence, curiosity, and courage wherever life takes you.

Ryu loved to play outside in the warm, sunny air.
He ran, climbed, and laughed all day long.

His big brother, Dash, was always right beside him.
They were the best adventure team.

One morning Ryu said, "Do I have to wear sunscreen?"
He made a little scrunchy face.

Dash laughed and said, "You don't want to get burned!"
"Trust me I've learned the hard way."

That night, Ryu had a dream about his skin.
It looked like a strong, shiny castle.

Suddenly, ZAP! Bright sun rays came zooming down!
"Oh no!" Ryu shouted.

Then a glowing friend appeared.
"I'm Sunny the Shield! I protect your skin!"

Sunny covered the castle like a soft, shiny blanket.
The sun rays bounced right off, BOING!

"They can't get us?" Ryu asked.
"Not if you put sunscreen on every day!" Sunny said.

Ryu woke up with a big smile.
"Dash! We need sunscreen!"

The brothers put sunscreen on their faces, arms, and legs.
"We're protecting our castles!" they cheered.

Now Ryu and Dash wear sunscreen before every adventure.

PARENT PRO TIP

Find a Sunscreen with Zinc Oxide & Titanium Dioxide

- Sunscreen should go on 15 minutes before sun exposure not right as you walk out the door.
- Kids need more sunscreen than you think, about a full shot glass amount to cover the whole body.
- "Waterproof" sunscreen isn't real. Look for water resistant and always reapply after swimming.
- Sunscreen expires! Check the date. Old sunscreen can lose effectiveness.
- Sprays are convenient, but lotions protect more evenly. (If using sprays rub them in after applying.)
- Lips burn too – use a lip balm with SPF.
- Most parents forget the sun is strongest between 10am-4pm even in cooler weather.

Protecting skin early is one of the easiest ways to prevent long term damage. Little steps now,

BIG PROTECTION FOR LIFE

Pack Your Sun Safety Bag

Draw a line or circle to what belongs in your beach bag.

Sun Safety Word Search

HAT

Can you find all the hidden sun safety words?

SUN

SKIN

SAFE

SUNNY

WATER

SPF

SHADE

Y U N Y Y V O F O G
S U N N Y A S I N E
U H A T E R A C S
N O I D H E F B P
V S H A D E R F
W K T T R O H A
S I I W A T E R
S N N Y S S E E

Draw Yourself Having Fun in the Sun!

Can you draw yourself enjoying a sunny day?
Don't forget your sun safety gear!

Sun Safety Scavenger Hunt!

Look carefully! Find and circle each item below.

Sun	Shady tree	Hat
Sunglasses	Water bottle	Sunscreen

Color Sunny the Skin Shield!

Help Sunny Get to the Soccer Field

Connect the Dots!

Follow the numbers and discover WHAT THE SURPRISE IS

Match the Colors!

Can you match each color to the correct objects?

Circle the Things That Start with "S"

Can you find everything that begins with the letter S ?

Color by Numbers

Share your sunscreen with your buddy and color the picture with the relevant colors

Sun Safety

Write the correct words on the lines

1. Always wear a __________  when you are in the sun.

2. __________ 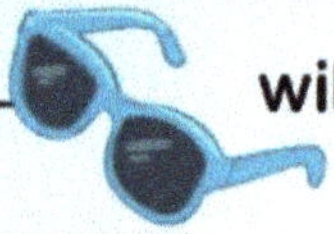 will help to protect your eyes from harmful rays of the sun.

3. Apply plenty of __________ 

to protect your skin from harmful rays.

4. After a few __________  you need to reapply.

5. Cover your skin with a __________ 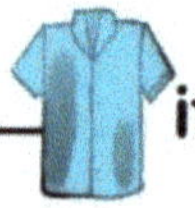 if you can.

6. Play in the __________  for even better protection from the sun.

shade	hat	hours	sunscreen	shirt	sunglasses

ABOUT THE AUTHOR

Sierra Jeffress is a creative storyteller with a passion for bringing imagination to life through meaningful, engaging narratives. With a background in aesthetics and plastic surgery industry, she blends science, care, and creativity into everything she does.

Inspired by her love for children and storytelling, Sierra writes books that spark curiosity, build confidence, and make learning fun. Her work focuses on turning everyday lessons - like sun safety - into magical, memorable adventures.

When she's not writing, Sierra enjoys spending time with her family, working in the world of advanced skincare and laser treatments, and creating content that educates and inspires others.

ABOUT THE ILLUSTRATOR

Farheen Fatima is a Canadian children's book illustrator who brings warmth, imagination, and charm to every page she creates. With a playful illustration style and a keen eye for detail, she transforms stories into engaging visual experiences that captivate young readers.

Passionate about visual storytelling, Farheen loves collaborating with authors and publishers to bring new tales to life through her artwork.

Ready to bring your story to life? Get in touch to discuss your project and create something children will treasure for years to come.

www.littlefolkstories.com

design@littlefolkstories.com

Scan to contact

www.ingramcontent.com/pod-product-compliance
Lightning Source LLC
LaVergne TN
LVHW071535210926
848349LV00013B/136
9798234103758

www.ingramcontent.com/pod-product-compliance
Lightning Source LLC
LaVergne TN
LVHW071535210926
848349LV00013B/136
9798234103758

DEDICATION

To my sons-
You are the reason behind every page, every word, and every dream brought to life in this story. You are my heart, my inspiration, and the reason these stories came to life. Watching you grow, learn, and shine brighter each day is my greatest joy. This book - and the series to come - begins with you and was written with love that will last far beyond these pages.

To every child-
May this story be a reminder that you are strong, bright, and protected. This is just the beginning of a series made to help you grow with confidence, curiosity, and courage wherever life takes you.

Ryu loved to play outside in the warm, sunny air.
He ran, climbed, and laughed all day long.

His big brother, Dash, was always right beside him.
They were the best adventure team.

One morning Ryu said, "Do I have to wear sunscreen?"
He made a little scrunchy face.

Dash laughed and said, "You don't want to get burned!"
"Trust me I've learned the hard way."

That night, Ryu had a dream about his skin.
It looked like a strong, shiny castle.

Suddenly, ZAP! Bright sun rays came zooming down!
"Oh no!" Ryu shouted.

Then a glowing friend appeared.
"I'm Sunny the Shield! I protect your skin!"

Sunny covered the castle like a soft, shiny blanket.
The sun rays bounced right off, BOING!

"They can't get us?" Ryu asked.
"Not if you put sunscreen on every day!" Sunny said.

Ryu woke up with a big smile.
"Dash! We need sunscreen!"

The brothers put sunscreen on their faces, arms, and legs.
"We're protecting our castles!" they cheered.

Now Ryu and Dash wear sunscreen before every adventure.

PARENT PRO TIP
Find a Sunscreen with
Zinc Oxide & Titanium Dioxide
ZINC OXIDE
TITANIUM DIOXIDE
HARMFUL UV RAYS
SUNSCREEN LAYER
SKIN SURFACE
SKIN CELLS
DEEPER SKIN LAYERS
They sit on top of the skin and block harmful rays like a tiny shield.
Sunscreen should go on 15 minutes before sun exposure not right as you walk out the door.
Kids need more sunscreen than you think, about a full shot glass amount to cover the whole body.
"Waterproof" sunscreen isn't real. Look for water resistant and always reapply after swimming.
OCT 26
Sunscreen expires! Check the date. Old sunscreen can lose effectiveness.
Sprays are convenient, but lotions protect more evenly. (If using sprays rub them in after applying.)
LIP BALM SPF
Lips burn too – use a lip balm with SPF.
Most parents forget the sun is strongest between 10am-4pm even in cooler weather.
SUNSCREEN SPF 50+
Protecting skin early is one of the easiest ways to prevent long term damage. Little steps now,
BIG PROTECTION FOR LIFE

Pack Your Sun Safety Bag

Draw a line or circle to what belongs in your beach bag.

Sun Safety Word Search

Can you find all the hidden sun safety words?

SUN
SKIN
SUNNY
SPF
HAT
SAFE
WATER
SHADE

Y U N Y Y V O F O G
S U N N Y A S I N E
U H A T E R A C S
N O I D H E F B P
V S H A D E R F
W K T T R O H A
S I I W A T E R
S N N Y S S E E

Draw Yourself Having Fun in the Sun!

**Can you draw yourself enjoying a sunny day?
Don't forget your sun safety gear!**

Sun Safety Scavenger Hunt!

Look carefully! Find and circle each item below.

Sun	Shady tree	Hat
Sunglasses	Water bottle	Sunscreen

Color Sunny the Skin Shield!

Help Sunny Get to the Soccer Field

Connect the Dots!

Follow the numbers and discover WHAT THE SURPRISE IS

Match the Colors!

Can you match each color to the correct objects?

Circle the Things That Start with "S"

Can you find everything that begins with the letter S ?

Color by Numbers

Share your sunscreen with your buddy and color the picture with the relevant colors

Sun Safety

Write the correct words on the lines

1. Always wear a __________  when you are in the sun.

2. __________ 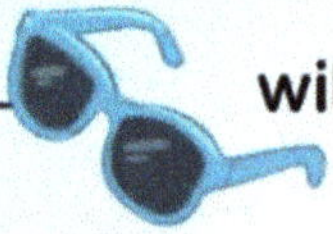 will help to protect your eyes from harmful rays of the sun.

3. Apply plenty of __________  to protect your skin from harmful rays.

4. After a few __________ 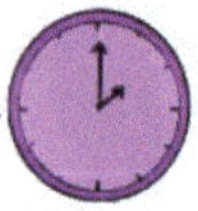 you need to reapply.

5. Cover your skin with a __________ 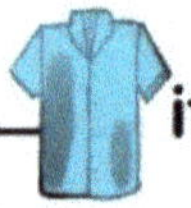 if you can.

6. Play in the __________  for even better protection from the sun.

shade	hat	hours	sunscreen	shirt	sunglasses

ABOUT THE AUTHOR

Sierra Jeffress is a creative storyteller with a passion for bringing imagination to life through meaningful, engaging narratives. With a background in aesthetics and plastic surgery industry, she blends science, care, and creativity into everything she does.

Inspired by her love for children and storytelling, Sierra writes books that spark curiosity, build confidence, and make learning fun. Her work focuses on turning everyday lessons - like sun safety - into magical, memorable adventures.

When she's not writing, Sierra enjoys spending time with her family, working in the world of advanced skincare and laser treatments, and creating content that educates and inspires others.

ABOUT THE ILLUSTRATOR

Farheen Fatima is a Canadian children's book illustrator who brings warmth, imagination, and charm to every page she creates. With a playful illustration style and a keen eye for detail, she transforms stories into engaging visual experiences that captivate young readers.

Passionate about visual storytelling, Farheen loves collaborating with authors and publishers to bring new tales to life through her artwork.

Ready to bring your story to life? Get in touch to discuss your project and create something children will treasure for years to come.

www.littlefolkstories.com

design@littlefolkstories.com

Scan to contact

www.ingramcontent.com/pod-product-compliance
Lightning Source LLC
LaVergne TN
LVHW071535210926
848349LV00013B/136

DEDICATION

To my sons-
You are the reason behind every page, every word, and every dream brought to life in this story. You are my heart, my inspiration, and the reason these stories came to life. Watching you grow, learn, and shine brighter each day is my greatest joy. This book - and the series to come - begins with you and was written with love that will last far beyond these pages.

To every child-
May this story be a reminder that you are strong, bright, and protected. This is just the beginning of a series made to help you grow with confidence, curiosity, and courage wherever life takes you.

Ryu loved to play outside in the warm, sunny air.
He ran, climbed, and laughed all day long.

His big brother, Dash, was always right beside him.
They were the best adventure team.

One morning Ryu said, "Do I have to wear sunscreen?"
He made a little scrunchy face.

Dash laughed and said, "You don't want to get burned!"
"Trust me I've learned the hard way."

That night, Ryu had a dream about his skin.
It looked like a strong, shiny castle.

Suddenly, ZAP! Bright sun rays came zooming down!
"Oh no!" Ryu shouted.

Then a glowing friend appeared.
"I'm Sunny the Shield! I protect your skin!"

Sunny covered the castle like a soft, shiny blanket.
The sun rays bounced right off, BOING!

"They can't get us?" Ryu asked.
"Not if you put sunscreen on every day!" Sunny said.

Ryu woke up with a big smile.
"Dash! We need sunscreen!"

The brothers put sunscreen on their faces, arms, and legs.
"We're protecting our castles!" they cheered.

Now Ryu and Dash wear sunscreen before every adventure.

PARENT PRO TIP
Find a Sunscreen with Zinc Oxide & Titanium Dioxide
ZINC OXIDE
TITANIUM DIOXIDE
HARMFUL UV RAYS
SUNSCREEN LAYER
SKIN SURFACE
SKIN CELLS
DEEPER SKIN LAYERS
They sit on top of the skin and block harmful rays like a tiny shield.
Sunscreen should go on 15 minutes before sun exposure not right as you walk out the door.
Kids need more sunscreen than you think, about a full shot glass amount to cover the whole body.
"Waterproof" sunscreen isn't real. Look for water resistant and always reapply after swimming.
OCT 26
Sunscreen expires! Check the date. Old sunscreen can lose effectiveness.
Sprays are convenient, but lotions protect more evenly. (if using sprays rub them in after applying.)
LIP BALM SPF
Lips burn too – use a lip balm with SPF.
Most parents forget the sun is strongest between 10am-4pm even in cooler weather.
SUNSCREEN SPF 50+
Protecting skin early is one of the easiest ways to prevent long term damage. Little steps now,
BIG PROTECTION FOR LIFE

Pack Your Sun Safety Bag

Draw a line or circle to what belongs in your beach bag.

Sun Safety Word Search

Can you find all the hidden sun safety words?

HAT

SUN

SKIN

SAFE

SUNNY

WATER

SPF

SHADE

Y	U	N	Y	Y	V	O	F	G
S	U	N	N	Y	A	S	I	N	E
U	H	A	T	E	R	A	C	S
N	O	I	D	H	E	F	B	P
V	S	H	A	D	E	R	F
W	K	T	T	R	O	H	A
S	I	I	W	A	T	E	R
S	N	N	Y	S	S	E	E

Draw Yourself Having Fun in the Sun!

Can you draw yourself enjoying a sunny day?
Don't forget your sun safety gear!

Sun Safety Scavenger Hunt!

Look carefully! Find and circle each item below.

Sun	Shady tree	Hat
Sunglasses	Water bottle	Sunscreen

Color Sunny the Skin Shield!

Help Sunny Get to the Soccer Field

Connect the Dots!

Follow the numbers and discover WHAT THE SURPRISE IS

Match the Colors!

Can you match each color to the correct objects?

Circle the Things That Start with "S"

Can you find everything that begins with the letter S ?

Color by Numbers

Share your sunscreen with your buddy and color the picture with the relevant colors

1 2 3 4 5 6 7 8 9

Sun Safety

Write the correct words on the lines

1. Always wear a ___________  when you are in the sun.

2. ___________ 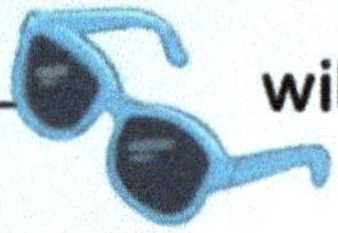 will help to protect your eyes from harmful rays of the sun.

3. Apply plenty of ___________ 

to protect your skin from harmful rays.

4. After a few ___________ 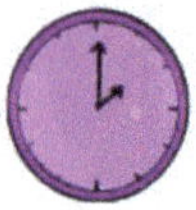 you need to reapply.

5. Cover your skin with a ___________ 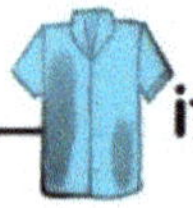 if you can.

6. Play in the ___________  for even better protection from the sun.

shade	hat	hours	sunscreen	shirt	sunglasses

ABOUT THE AUTHOR

Sierra Jeffress is a creative storyteller with a passion for bringing imagination to life through meaningful, engaging narratives. With a background in aesthetics and plastic surgery industry, she blends science, care, and creativity into everything she does.

Inspired by her love for children and storytelling, Sierra writes books that spark curiosity, build confidence, and make learning fun. Her work focuses on turning everyday lessons - like sun safety - into magical, memorable adventures.

When she's not writing, Sierra enjoys spending time with her family, working in the world of advanced skincare and laser treatments, and creating content that educates and inspires others.

ABOUT THE ILLUSTRATOR

Farheen Fatima is a Canadian children's book illustrator who brings warmth, imagination, and charm to every page she creates. With a playful illustration style and a keen eye for detail, she transforms stories into engaging visual experiences that captivate young readers.

Passionate about visual storytelling, Farheen loves collaborating with authors and publishers to bring new tales to life through her artwork.

Ready to bring your story to life? Get in touch to discuss your project and create something children will treasure for years to come.

www.littlefolkstories.com

design@littlefolkstories.com

Scan to contact

www.ingramcontent.com/pod-product-compliance
Lightning Source LLC
LaVergne TN
LVHW071535210926
848349LV00013B/136
* 9 7 9 8 2 3 4 1 0 3 7 5 8 *

SUNNY the SKIN SHIELD

Dedication

To my sons–
You are the reason behind every page, every word, and every dream brought to life in this story. You are my heart, my inspiration, and the reason these stories came to life. Watching you grow, learn, and shine brighter each day is my greatest joy. This book - and the series to come - begins with you and was written with love that will last far beyond these pages.

To every child–
May this story be a reminder that you are strong, bright, and protected. This is just the beginning of a series made to help you grow with confidence, curiosity, and courage wherever life takes you.

Ryu loved to play outside in the warm, sunny air.
He ran, climbed, and laughed all day long.

His big brother, Dash, was always right beside him.
They were the best adventure team.

One morning Ryu said, "Do I have to wear sunscreen?"
He made a little scrunchy face.

Dash laughed and said, "You don't want to get burned!"
"Trust me I've learned the hard way."

That night, Ryu had a dream about his skin.
It looked like a strong, shiny castle.

Suddenly, ZAP! Bright sun rays came zooming down!
"Oh no!" Ryu shouted.

Then a glowing friend appeared.
"I'm Sunny the Shield! I protect your skin!"

Sunny covered the castle like a soft, shiny blanket.
The sun rays bounced right off, BOING!

"They can't get us?" Ryu asked.
"Not if you put sunscreen on every day!" Sunny said.

Ryu woke up with a big smile.
"Dash! We need sunscreen!"

The brothers put sunscreen on their faces, arms, and legs.
"We're protecting our castles!" they cheered.

Now Ryu and Dash wear sunscreen before every adventure.

PARENT PRO TIP

Find a Sunscreen with Zinc Oxide & Titanium Dioxide

- Sunscreen should go on 15 minutes before sun exposure not right as you walk out the door.
- Kids need more sunscreen than you think, about a full shot glass amount to cover the whole body.
- "Waterproof" sunscreen isn't real. Look for water resistant and always reapply after swimming.
- OCT 26 — Sunscreen expires! Check the date. Old sunscreen can lose effectiveness.
- Sprays are convenient, but lotions protect more evenly. (If using sprays rub them in after applying.)
- LIP BALM SPF — Lips burn too – use a lip balm with SPF.
- Most parents forget the sun is strongest between 10am-4pm even in cooler weather.

Protecting skin early is one of the easiest ways to prevent long term damage. Little steps now,

BIG PROTECTION FOR LIFE

SUNSCREEN SPF 50+

Pack Your Sun Safety Bag

Draw a line or circle to what belongs in your beach bag.

Sun Safety Word Search

Can you find all the hidden sun safety words?

SUN

SKIN

SUNNY

HAT

SAFE

WATER

SHADE

SPF

Y U N Y Y V O F O G

S U N N Y A S I N E

U H A T E R A C S

N O I D H E F B P

V S H A D E R F

W K T T R O H A

S I I W A T E R

S N N Y S S E E

Draw Yourself Having Fun in the Sun!

Can you draw yourself enjoying a sunny day?
Don't forget your sun safety gear!

Sun Safety Scavenger Hunt!

Look carefully! Find and circle each item below.

Sun	Shady tree	Hat
Sunglasses	Water bottle	Sunscreen

Color Sunny the Skin Shield!

Help Sunny Get to the Soccer Field

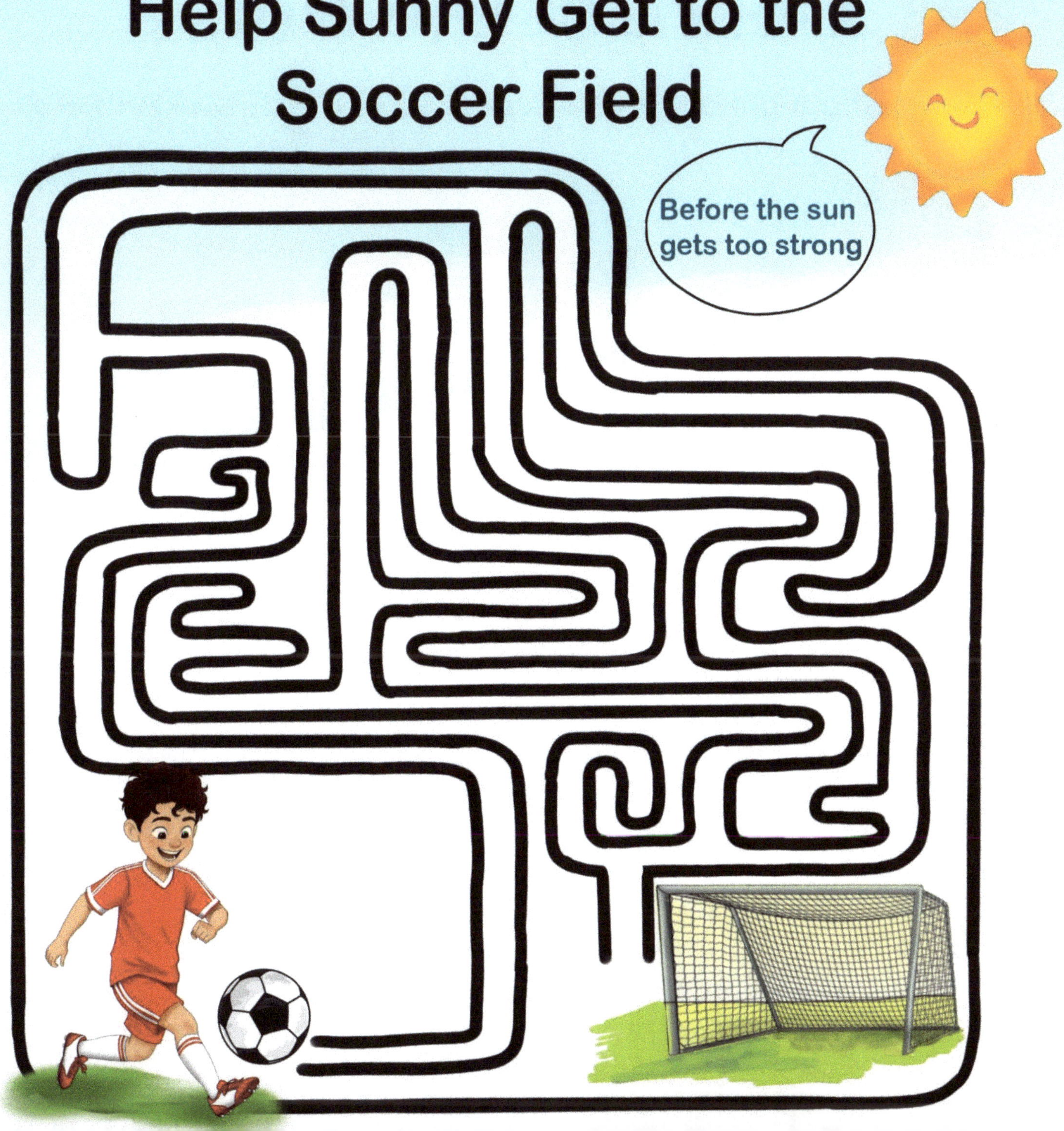

Connect the Dots!

Follow the numbers and discover WHAT THE SURPRISE IS

Match the Colors!

Can you match each color to the correct objects?

Circle the Things That Start with "S"

Can you find everything that begins with the letter S ?

Color by Numbers

Share your sunscreen with your buddy and color the picture with the relevant colors

Sun Safety

Write the correct words on the lines

1. Always wear a ________  when you are in the sun.

2. ____________  will help to protect your eyes from harmful rays of the sun.

3. Apply plenty of ____________ 

to protect your skin from harmful rays.

4. After a few ____________  you need to reapply.

5. Cover your skin with a ____________  if you can.

6. Play in the ____________  for even better protection from the sun.

shade	hat	hours	sunscreen	shirt	sunglasses

ABOUT THE AUTHOR

Sierra Jeffress is a creative storyteller with a passion for bringing imagination to life through meaningful, engaging narratives. With a background in aesthetics and plastic surgery industry, she blends science, care, and creativity into everything she does.

Inspired by her love for children and storytelling, Sierra writes books that spark curiosity, build confidence, and make learning fun. Her work focuses on turning everyday lessons - like sun safety - into magical, memorable adventures.

When she's not writing, Sierra enjoys spending time with her family, working in the world of advanced skincare and laser treatments, and creating content that educates and inspires others.

ABOUT THE ILLUSTRATOR

Farheen Fatima is a Canadian children's book illustrator who brings warmth, imagination, and charm to every page she creates. With a playful illustration style and a keen eye for detail, she transforms stories into engaging visual experiences that captivate young readers.

Passionate about visual storytelling, Farheen loves collaborating with authors and publishers to bring new tales to life through her artwork.

Ready to bring your story to life? Get in touch to discuss your project and create something children will treasure for years to come.

www.littlefolkstories.com

design@littlefolkstories.com

Scan to contact

www.ingramcontent.com/pod-product-compliance
Lightning Source LLC
LaVergne TN
LVHW071535210926
848349LV00013B/136

SUNNY the SKIN SHIELD

DEDICATION

To my sons-

You are the reason behind every page, every word, and every dream brought to life in this story. You are my heart, my inspiration, and the reason these stories came to life. Watching you grow, learn, and shine brighter each day is my greatest joy. This book - and the series to come - begins with you and was written with love that will last far beyond these pages.

To every child-

May this story be a reminder that you are strong, bright, and protected. This is just the beginning of a series made to help you grow with confidence, curiosity, and courage wherever life takes you.

Ryu loved to play outside in the warm, sunny air.
He ran, climbed, and laughed all day long.

His big brother, Dash, was always right beside him.
They were the best adventure team.

One morning Ryu said, "Do I have to wear sunscreen?"
He made a little scrunchy face.

Dash laughed and said, "You don't want to get burned!"
"Trust me I've learned the hard way."

That night, Ryu had a dream about his skin.
It looked like a strong, shiny castle.

Suddenly, ZAP! Bright sun rays came zooming down!
"Oh no!" Ryu shouted.

Then a glowing friend appeared.
"I'm Sunny the Shield! I protect your skin!"

Sunny covered the castle like a soft, shiny blanket.
The sun rays bounced right off, BOING!

"They can't get us?" Ryu asked.
"Not if you put sunscreen on every day!" Sunny said.

Ryu woke up with a big smile.
"Dash! We need sunscreen!"

The brothers put sunscreen on their faces, arms, and legs.
"We're protecting our castles!" they cheered.

Now Ryu and Dash wear sunscreen before every adventure.

PARENT PRO TIP

Find a Sunscreen with Zinc Oxide & Titanium Dioxide

- Sunscreen should go on 15 minutes before sun exposure not right as you walk out the door.
- Kids need more sunscreen than you think, about a full shot glass amount to cover the whole body.
- "Waterproof" sunscreen isn't real. Look for water resistant and always reapply after swimming.
- Sunscreen expires! Check the date. Old sunscreen can lose effectiveness.
- Sprays are convenient, but lotions protect more evenly. (if using sprays rub them in after applying.)
- Lips burn too – use a lip balm with SPF.
- Most parents forget the sun is strongest between 10am-4pm even in cooler weather.

Protecting skin early is one of the easiest ways to prevent long term damage. Little steps now,

BIG PROTECTION FOR LIFE

Pack Your Sun Safety Bag

Draw a line or circle to what belongs in your beach bag.

Sun Safety Word Search

Can you find all the hidden sun safety words?

- SUN
- SKIN
- SUNNY
- SPF
- HAT
- SAFE
- WATER
- SHADE

Y U N Y Y V O F O G
S U N N Y A S I N E
U H A T E R A C S
N O I D H E F B P
V S H A D E R F
W K T T R O H A
S I I W A T E R
S N N Y S S E E

Draw Yourself Having Fun in the Sun!

Can you draw yourself enjoying a sunny day?
Don't forget your sun safety gear!

Sun Safety Scavenger Hunt!

Look carefully! Find and circle each item below.

Sun	Shady tree	Hat
Sunglasses	Water bottle	Sunscreen

Color Sunny the Skin Shield!

Help Sunny Get to the Soccer Field

Connect the Dots!

Follow the numbers and discover WHAT THE SURPRISE IS

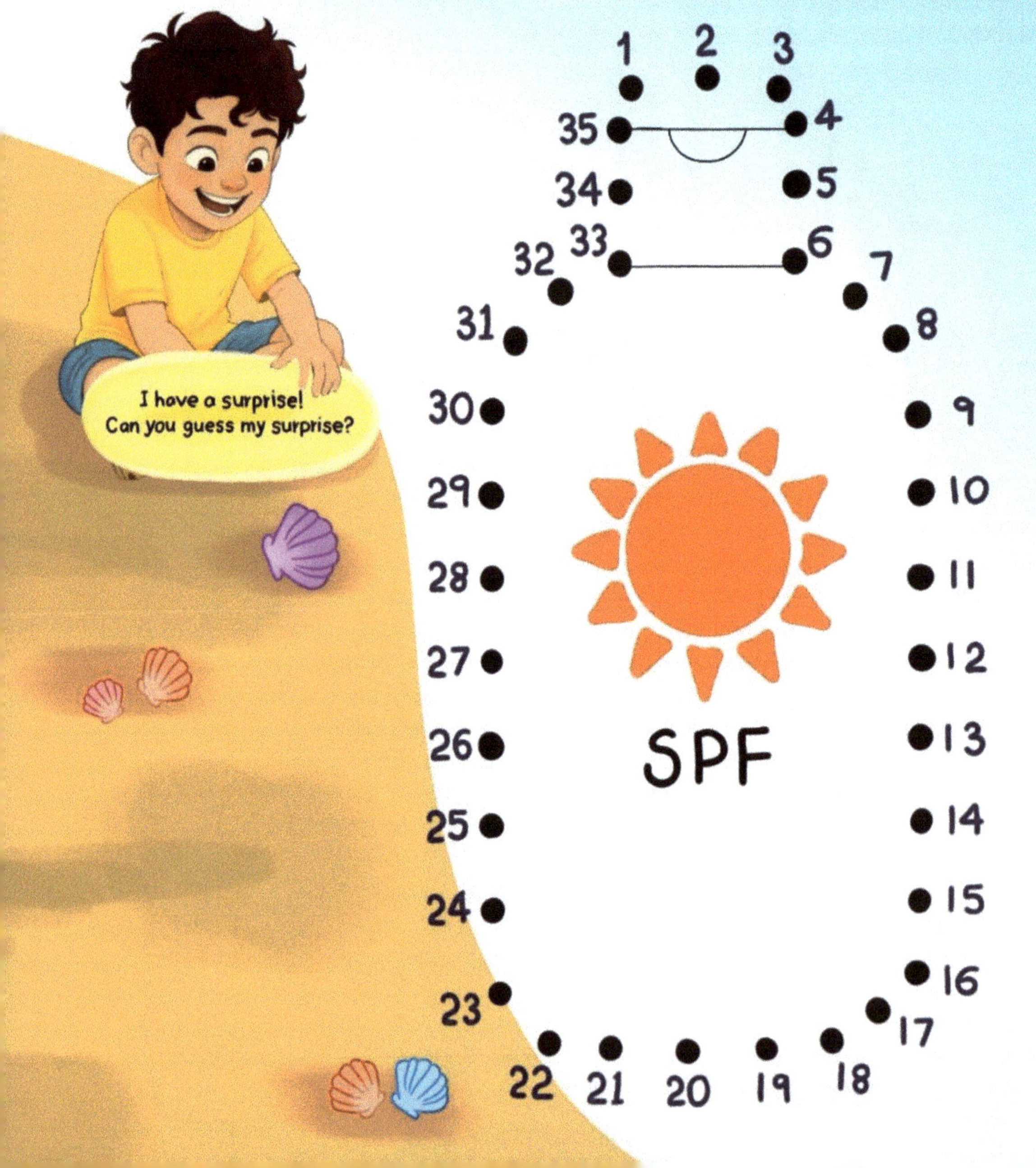

Match the Colors!

Can you match each color to the correct objects?

Circle the Things That Start with "S"

Can you find everything that begins with the letter S ?

Color by Numbers

Share your sunscreen with your buddy and color the picture with the relevant colors

Sun Safety

Write the correct words on the lines

1. Always wear a ________  when you are in the sun.

2. ________ 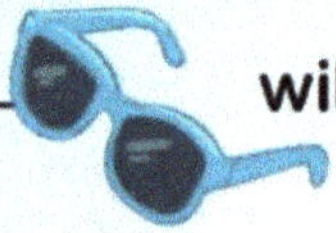 will help to protect your eyes from harmful rays of the sun.

3. Apply plenty of ________ 

to protect your skin from harmful rays.

4. After a few ________  you need to reapply.

5. Cover your skin with a ________  if you can.

6. Play in the ________  for even better protection from the sun.

shade	hat	hours	sunscreen	shirt	sunglasses

ABOUT THE AUTHOR

Sierra Jeffress is a creative storyteller with a passion for bringing imagination to life through meaningful, engaging narratives. With a background in aesthetics and plastic surgery industry, she blends science, care, and creativity into everything she does.

Inspired by her love for children and storytelling, Sierra writes books that spark curiosity, build confidence, and make learning fun. Her work focuses on turning everyday lessons - like sun safety - into magical, memorable adventures.

When she's not writing, Sierra enjoys spending time with her family, working in the world of advanced skincare and laser treatments, and creating content that educates and inspires others.

ABOUT THE ILLUSTRATOR

Farheen Fatima is a Canadian children's book illustrator who brings warmth, imagination, and charm to every page she creates. With a playful illustration style and a keen eye for detail, she transforms stories into engaging visual experiences that captivate young readers.

Passionate about visual storytelling, Farheen loves collaborating with authors and publishers to bring new tales to life through her artwork.

Ready to bring your story to life? Get in touch to discuss your project and create something children will treasure for years to come.

www.littlefolkstories.com

design@littlefolkstories.com

Scan to contact

www.ingramcontent.com/pod-product-compliance
Lightning Source LLC
LaVergne TN
LVHW071535210926
848349LV00013B/136

SUNNY the SKIN SHIELD

DEDICATION

To my sons-

You are the reason behind every page, every word, and every dream brought to life in this story. You are my heart, my inspiration, and the reason these stories came to life. Watching you grow, learn, and shine brighter each day is my greatest joy. This book - and the series to come - begins with you and was written with love that will last far beyond these pages.

To every child-

May this story be a reminder that you are strong, bright, and protected. This is just the beginning of a series made to help you grow with confidence, curiosity, and courage wherever life takes you.

Ryu loved to play outside in the warm, sunny air.
He ran, climbed, and laughed all day long.

His big brother, Dash, was always right beside him.
They were the best adventure team.

One morning Ryu said, "Do I have to wear sunscreen?"
He made a little scrunchy face.

Dash laughed and said, "You don't want to get burned!"
"Trust me I've learned the hard way."

That night, Ryu had a dream about his skin.
It looked like a strong, shiny castle.

Suddenly, ZAP! Bright sun rays came zooming down!
"Oh no!" Ryu shouted.

Then a glowing friend appeared.
"I'm Sunny the Shield! I protect your skin!"

Sunny covered the castle like a soft, shiny blanket.
The sun rays bounced right off, BOING!

"They can't get us?" Ryu asked.
"Not if you put sunscreen on every day!" Sunny said.

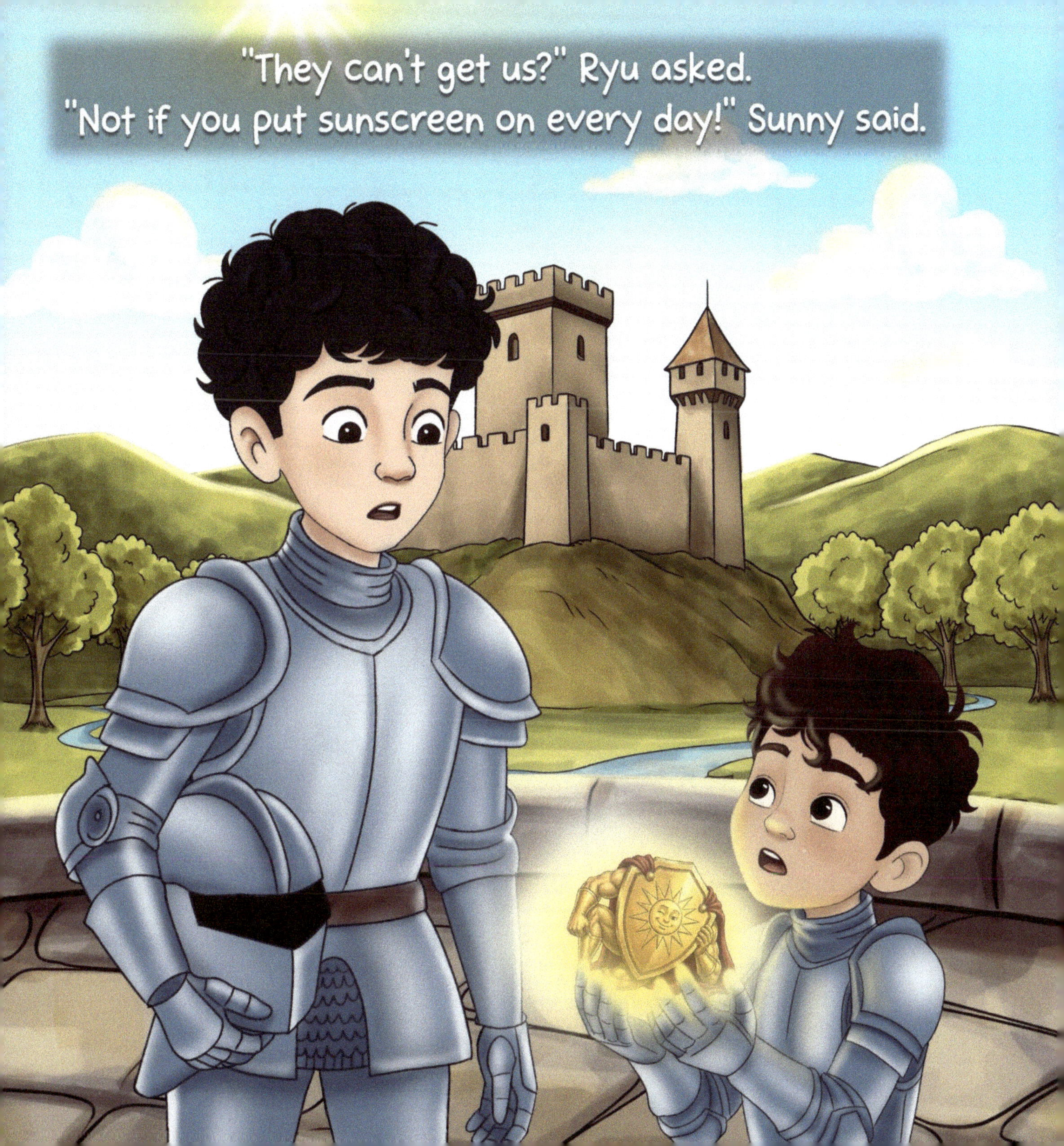

Ryu woke up with a big smile.
"Dash! We need sunscreen!"

The brothers put sunscreen on their faces, arms, and legs.
"We're protecting our castles!" they cheered.

Now Ryu and Dash wear sunscreen before every adventure.

PARENT PRO TIP
Find a Sunscreen with
Zinc Oxide & Titanium Dioxide
ZINC OXIDE
TITANIUM DIOXIDE
HARMFUL UV RAYS
SUNSCREEN LAYER
SKIN SURFACE
SKIN CELLS
DEEPER SKIN LAYERS
They sit on top of the skin and block harmful rays like a tiny shield.
Sunscreen should go on 15 minutes before sun exposure not right as you walk out the door.
Kids need more sunscreen than you think, about a full shot glass amount to cover the whole body.
"Waterproof" sunscreen isn't real. Look for water resistant and always reapply after swimming.
OCT 26
Sunscreen expires! Check the date. Old sunscreen can lose effectiveness.
Sprays are convenient, but lotions protect more evenly. (If using sprays rub them in after applying.)
LIP BALM SPF
Lips burn too – use a lip balm with SPF.
Most parents forget the sun is strongest between 10am-4pm even in cooler weather.
SUNSCREEN SPF 50+
Protecting skin early is one of the easiest ways to prevent long term damage. Little steps now,
BIG PROTECTION FOR LIFE

Pack Your Sun Safety Bag

Draw a line or circle to what belongs in your beach bag.

Sun Safety Word Search

Can you find all the hidden sun safety words?

Y U N Y Y V O F O G
S U N N Y A S I N E
U H A T E R A C S
N O I D H E F B P
V S H A D E R F
W K T T R O H A
S I I W A T E R
S N N Y S S E E

SUN
SKIN
SUNNY
SPF
HAT
SAFE
WATER
SHADE

Draw Yourself Having Fun in the Sun!

Can you draw yourself enjoying a sunny day?
Don't forget your sun safety gear!

Sun Safety Scavenger Hunt!

Look carefully! Find and circle each item below.

Sun	Shady tree	Hat
Sunglasses	Water bottle	Sunscreen

Color Sunny the Skin Shield!

Help Sunny Get to the Soccer Field

Connect the Dots!

Follow the numbers and discover WHAT THE SURPRISE IS

Match the Colors!

Can you match each color to the correct objects?

Circle the Things That Start with "S"

Can you find everything that begins with the letter S ?

Color by Numbers

Share your sunscreen with your buddy and color the picture with the relevant colors

Sun Safety

Write the correct words on the lines

1. Always wear a ____________  when you are in the sun.

2. ________________ 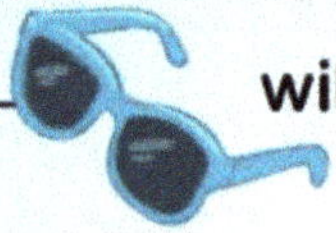 will help to protect your eyes from harmful rays of the sun.

3. Apply plenty of ________________ 

to protect your skin from harmful rays.

4. After a few ________________ 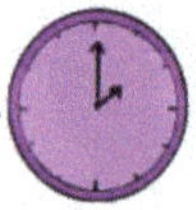 you need to reapply.

5. Cover your skin with a ________________ 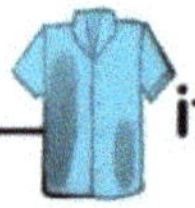 if you can.

6. Play in the ________________  for even better protection from the sun.

shade	hat	hours	sunscreen	shirt	sunglasses

ABOUT THE AUTHOR

Sierra Jeffress is a creative storyteller with a passion for bringing imagination to life through meaningful, engaging narratives. With a background in aesthetics and plastic surgery industry, she blends science, care, and creativity into everything she does.

Inspired by her love for children and storytelling, Sierra writes books that spark curiosity, build confidence, and make learning fun. Her work focuses on turning everyday lessons - like sun safety - into magical, memorable adventures.

When she's not writing, Sierra enjoys spending time with her family, working in the world of advanced skincare and laser treatments, and creating content that educates and inspires others.

ABOUT THE ILLUSTRATOR

Farheen Fatima is a Canadian children's book illustrator who brings warmth, imagination, and charm to every page she creates. With a playful illustration style and a keen eye for detail, she transforms stories into engaging visual experiences that captivate young readers.

Passionate about visual storytelling, Farheen loves collaborating with authors and publishers to bring new tales to life through her artwork.

Ready to bring your story to life? Get in touch to discuss your project and create something children will treasure for years to come.

www.littlefolkstories.com

design@littlefolkstories.com

Scan to contact

www.ingramcontent.com/pod-product-compliance
Lightning Source LLC
LaVergne TN
LVHW071535210926
848349LV00013B/136
* 9 7 9 8 2 3 4 1 0 3 7 5 8 *

SUNNY the SKIN SHIELD

DEDICATION

To my sons-
You are the reason behind every page, every word, and every dream brought to life in this story. You are my heart, my inspiration, and the reason these stories came to life. Watching you grow, learn, and shine brighter each day is my greatest joy. This book - and the series to come - begins with you and was written with love that will last far beyond these pages.

To every child-
May this story be a reminder that you are strong, bright, and protected. This is just the beginning of a series made to help you grow with confidence, curiosity, and courage wherever life takes you.

Ryu loved to play outside in the warm, sunny air.
He ran, climbed, and laughed all day long.

His big brother, Dash, was always right beside him.
They were the best adventure team.

One morning Ryu said, "Do I have to wear sunscreen?"
He made a little scrunchy face.

Dash laughed and said, "You don't want to get burned!"
"Trust me I've learned the hard way."

That night, Ryu had a dream about his skin.
It looked like a strong, shiny castle.

Suddenly, ZAP! Bright sun rays came zooming down!
"Oh no!" Ryu shouted.

Then a glowing friend appeared.
"I'm Sunny the Shield! I protect your skin!"

Sunny covered the castle like a soft, shiny blanket.
The sun rays bounced right off, BOING!

"They can't get us?" Ryu asked.
"Not if you put sunscreen on every day!" Sunny said.

Ryu woke up with a big smile.
"Dash! We need sunscreen!"

The brothers put sunscreen on their faces, arms, and legs. "We're protecting our castles!" they cheered.

Now Ryu and Dash wear sunscreen before every adventure.

PARENT PRO TIP

Find a Sunscreen with Zinc Oxide & Titanium Dioxide

- Sunscreen should go on 15 minutes before sun exposure not right as you walk out the door.
- Kids need more sunscreen than you think, about a full shot glass amount to cover the whole body.
- "Waterproof" sunscreen isn't real. Look for water resistant and always reapply after swimming.
- Sunscreen expires! Check the date. Old sunscreen can lose effectiveness.
- Sprays are convenient, but lotions protect more evenly. (If using sprays rub them in after applying.)
- Lips burn too – use a lip balm with SPF.
- Most parents forget the sun is strongest between 10am-4pm even in cooler weather.

Protecting skin early is one of the easiest ways to prevent long term damage. Little steps now,

BIG PROTECTION FOR LIFE

Pack Your Sun Safety Bag

Draw a line or circle to what belongs in your beach bag.

Sun Safety Word Search

Can you find all the hidden sun safety words?

HAT

SUN

SKIN

SAFE

SUNNY

WATER

SPF

SHADE

Y U N Y Y V O F O G
S U N N Y A S I N E
U H A T E R A C S
N O I D H E F B P
V S H A D E R F
W K T T R O H A
S I I W A T E R
S N N Y S S E E

Draw Yourself Having Fun in the Sun!

Can you draw yourself enjoying a sunny day?
Don't forget your sun safety gear!

Sun Safety Scavenger Hunt!

Look carefully! Find and circle each item below.

Sun	Shady tree	Hat
Sunglasses	Water bottle	Sunscreen

Color Sunny the Skin Shield!

Help Sunny Get to the Soccer Field

Connect the Dots!

Follow the numbers and discover WHAT THE SURPRISE IS

Match the Colors!

Can you match each color to the correct objects?

Circle the Things That Start with "S"

Can you find everything that begins with the letter S ?

Color by Numbers

Share your sunscreen with your buddy and color the picture with the relevant colors

1 2 3 4 5 6 7 8 9

Sun Safety

Write the correct words on the lines

1. Always wear a __________  when you are in the sun.

2. __________ 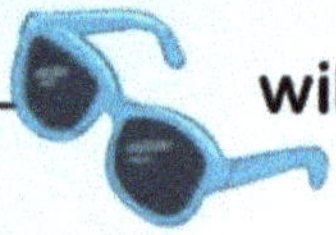 will help to protect your eyes from harmful rays of the sun.

3. Apply plenty of __________ 

to protect your skin from harmful rays.

4. After a few __________  you need to reapply.

5. Cover your skin with a __________  if you can.

6. Play in the __________  for even better protection from the sun.

shade	hat	hours	sunscreen	shirt	sunglasses

ABOUT THE AUTHOR

Sierra Jeffress is a creative storyteller with a passion for bringing imagination to life through meaningful, engaging narratives. With a background in aesthetics and plastic surgery industry, she blends science, care, and creativity into everything she does.

Inspired by her love for children and storytelling, Sierra writes books that spark curiosity, build confidence, and make learning fun. Her work focuses on turning everyday lessons - like sun safety - into magical, memorable adventures.

When she's not writing, Sierra enjoys spending time with her family, working in the world of advanced skincare and laser treatments, and creating content that educates and inspires others.

ABOUT THE ILLUSTRATOR

Farheen Fatima is a Canadian children's book illustrator who brings warmth, imagination, and charm to every page she creates. With a playful illustration style and a keen eye for detail, she transforms stories into engaging visual experiences that captivate young readers.

Passionate about visual storytelling, Farheen loves collaborating with authors and publishers to bring new tales to life through her artwork.

Ready to bring your story to life? Get in touch to discuss your project and create something children will treasure for years to come.

www.littlefolkstories.com

design@littlefolkstories.com

Scan to contact

www.ingramcontent.com/pod-product-compliance
Lightning Source LLC
LaVergne TN
LVHW071535210926
848349LV00013B/136

DEDICATION

To my sons-
You are the reason behind every page, every word, and every dream brought to life in this story. You are my heart, my inspiration, and the reason these stories came to life. Watching you grow, learn, and shine brighter each day is my greatest joy. This book - and the series to come - begins with you and was written with love that will last far beyond these pages.

To every child-
May this story be a reminder that you are strong, bright, and protected. This is just the beginning of a series made to help you grow with confidence, curiosity, and courage wherever life takes you.

Ryu loved to play outside in the warm, sunny air.
He ran, climbed, and laughed all day long.

His big brother, Dash, was always right beside him.
They were the best adventure team.

One morning Ryu said, "Do I have to wear sunscreen?"
He made a little scrunchy face.

Dash laughed and said, "You don't want to get burned!"
"Trust me I've learned the hard way."

That night, Ryu had a dream about his skin.
It looked like a strong, shiny castle.

Suddenly, ZAP! Bright sun rays came zooming down!
"Oh no!" Ryu shouted.

Then a glowing friend appeared.
"I'm Sunny the Shield! I protect your skin!"

Sunny covered the castle like a soft, shiny blanket.
The sun rays bounced right off, BOING!

"They can't get us?" Ryu asked.
"Not if you put sunscreen on every day!" Sunny said.

Ryu woke up with a big smile.
"Dash! We need sunscreen!"

The brothers put sunscreen on their faces, arms, and legs.
"We're protecting our castles!" they cheered.

Now Ryu and Dash wear sunscreen before every adventure.

PARENT PRO TIP

Find a Sunscreen with Zinc Oxide & Titanium Dioxide

- Sunscreen should go on 15 minutes before sun exposure not right as you walk out the door.
- Kids need more sunscreen than you think, about a full shot glass amount to cover the whole body.
- "Waterproof" sunscreen isn't real. Look for water resistant and always reapply after swimming.
- Sunscreen expires! Check the date. Old sunscreen can lose effectiveness.
- Sprays are convenient, but lotions protect more evenly. (if using sprays rub them in after applying.)
- Lips burn too – use a lip balm with SPF.
- Most parents forget the sun is strongest between 10am-4pm even in cooler weather.

Protecting skin early is one of the easiest ways to prevent long term damage. Little steps now,

BIG PROTECTION FOR LIFE

Pack Your Sun Safety Bag

Draw a line or circle to what belongs in your beach bag.

Sun Safety Word Search

HAT

Can you find all the hidden sun safety words?

SUN

SKIN

SAFE

SUNNY

WATER

SPF

SHADE

Y U N Y Y V O F O G
S U N N Y A S I N E
U H A T E R A C S
N O I D H E F B P
V S H A D E R F
W K T T R O H A
S I I W A T E R
S N N Y S S E E

Draw Yourself Having Fun in the Sun!

Can you draw yourself enjoying a sunny day?
Don't forget your sun safety gear!

Sun Safety Scavenger Hunt!

Look carefully! Find and circle each item below.

Sun	Shady tree	Hat
Sunglasses	Water bottle	Sunscreen

Color Sunny the Skin Shield!

Help Sunny Get to the Soccer Field

Connect the Dots!

Follow the numbers and discover WHAT THE SURPRISE IS

Match the Colors!

Can you match each color to the correct objects?

Circle the Things That Start with "S"

Can you find everything that begins with the letter S ?

Color by Numbers

Share your sunscreen with your buddy and color the picture with the relevant colors

Sun Safety

Write the correct words on the lines

1. Always wear a __________  when you are in the sun.

2. __________ 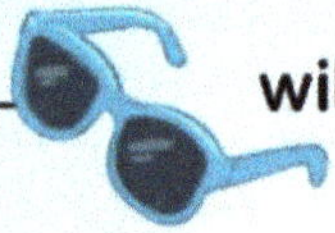 will help to protect your eyes from harmful rays of the sun.

3. Apply plenty of __________ 

to protect your skin from harmful rays.

4. After a few __________  you need to reapply.

5. Cover your skin with a __________ 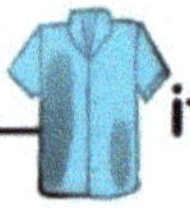 if you can.

6. Play in the __________  for even better protection from the sun.

shade	hat	hours	sunscreen	shirt	sunglasses

ABOUT THE AUTHOR

Sierra Jeffress is a creative storyteller with a passion for bringing imagination to life through meaningful, engaging narratives. With a background in aesthetics and plastic surgery industry, she blends science, care, and creativity into everything she does.

Inspired by her love for children and storytelling, Sierra writes books that spark curiosity, build confidence, and make learning fun. Her work focuses on turning everyday lessons - like sun safety - into magical, memorable adventures.

When she's not writing, Sierra enjoys spending time with her family, working in the world of advanced skincare and laser treatments, and creating content that educates and inspires others.

ABOUT THE ILLUSTRATOR

Farheen Fatima is a Canadian children's book illustrator who brings warmth, imagination, and charm to every page she creates. With a playful illustration style and a keen eye for detail, she transforms stories into engaging visual experiences that captivate young readers.

Passionate about visual storytelling, Farheen loves collaborating with authors and publishers to bring new tales to life through her artwork.

Ready to bring your story to life? Get in touch to discuss your project and create something children will treasure for years to come.

www.littlefolkstories.com

design@littlefolkstories.com

Scan to contact

www.ingramcontent.com/pod-product-compliance
Lightning Source LLC
LaVergne TN
LVHW071535210926
848349LV00013B/136

Dedication

To my sons-

You are the reason behind every page, every word, and every dream brought to life in this story. You are my heart, my inspiration, and the reason these stories came to life. Watching you grow, learn, and shine brighter each day is my greatest joy. This book - and the series to come - begins with you and was written with love that will last far beyond these pages.

To every child-

May this story be a reminder that you are strong, bright, and protected. This is just the beginning of a series made to help you grow with confidence, curiosity, and courage wherever life takes you.

Ryu loved to play outside in the warm, sunny air.
He ran, climbed, and laughed all day long.

His big brother, Dash, was always right beside him.
They were the best adventure team.

One morning Ryu said, "Do I have to wear sunscreen?"
He made a little scrunchy face.

Dash laughed and said, "You don't want to get burned!"
"Trust me I've learned the hard way."

That night, Ryu had a dream about his skin.
It looked like a strong, shiny castle.

Suddenly, ZAP! Bright sun rays came zooming down!
"Oh no!" Ryu shouted.

Then a glowing friend appeared.
"I'm Sunny the Shield! I protect your skin!"

Sunny covered the castle like a soft, shiny blanket.
The sun rays bounced right off, BOING!

"They can't get us?" Ryu asked.
"Not if you put sunscreen on every day!" Sunny said.

Ryu woke up with a big smile.
"Dash! We need sunscreen!"

The brothers put sunscreen on their faces, arms, and legs. "We're protecting our castles!" they cheered.

Now Ryu and Dash wear sunscreen before every adventure.

PARENT PRO TIP
Find a Sunscreen with Zinc Oxide & Titanium Dioxide
ZINC OXIDE
TITANIUM DIOXIDE
HARMFUL UV RAYS
SUNSCREEN LAYER
SKIN SURFACE
SKIN CELLS
DEEPER SKIN LAYERS
They sit on top of the skin and block harmful rays like a tiny shield.
Sunscreen should go on 15 minutes before sun exposure not right as you walk out the door.
Kids need more sunscreen than you think, about a full shot glass amount to cover the whole body.
"Waterproof" sunscreen isn't real. Look for water resistant and always reapply after swimming.
OCT 26
Sunscreen expires! Check the date. Old sunscreen can lose effectiveness.
Sprays are convenient, but lotions protect more evenly. (if using sprays rub them in after applying.)
LIP BALM SPF
Lips burn too – use a lip balm with SPF.
Most parents forget the sun is strongest between 10am-4pm even in cooler weather.
SUNSCREEN SPF 50+
Protecting skin early is one of the easiest ways to prevent long term damage. Little steps now,
BIG PROTECTION FOR LIFE

Pack Your Sun Safety Bag

Draw a line or circle to what belongs in your beach bag.

Sun Safety Word Search

Can you find all the hidden sun safety words?

Y U N Y Y V O F O G
S U N N Y A S I N E
U H A T E R A C S
N O I D H E F B P
V S H A D E R F
W K T T R O H A
S I I W A T E R
S N N Y S S E E

SUN
SKIN
SUNNY
SPF
HAT
SAFE
WATER
SHADE

Draw Yourself Having Fun in the Sun!

Can you draw yourself enjoying a sunny day?
Don't forget your sun safety gear!

Sun Safety Scavenger Hunt!

Look carefully! Find and circle each item below.

Sun	Shady tree	Hat
Sunglasses	Water bottle	Sunscreen

Color Sunny the Skin Shield!

Help Sunny Get to the Soccer Field

Connect the Dots!

Follow the numbers and discover WHAT THE SURPRISE IS

Match the Colors!

Can you match each color to the correct objects?

Circle the Things That Start with "S"

Can you find everything that begins with the letter S ?

Color by Numbers

Share your sunscreen with your buddy and color the picture with the relevant colors

Sun Safety

Write the correct words on the lines

1. Always wear a ____________  when you are in the sun.

2. ________________ 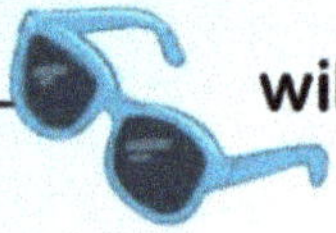 will help to protect your eyes from harmful rays of the sun.

3. Apply plenty of ________________  to protect your skin from harmful rays.

4. After a few ________________  you need to reapply.

5. Cover your skin with a ________________ 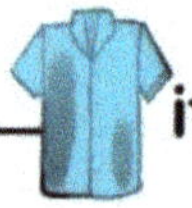 if you can.

6. Play in the ________________  for even better protection from the sun.

shade	hat	hours	sunscreen	shirt	sunglasses

ABOUT THE AUTHOR

Sierra Jeffress is a creative storyteller with a passion for bringing imagination to life through meaningful, engaging narratives. With a background in aesthetics and plastic surgery industry, she blends science, care, and creativity into everything she does.

Inspired by her love for children and storytelling, Sierra writes books that spark curiosity, build confidence, and make learning fun. Her work focuses on turning everyday lessons - like sun safety - into magical, memorable adventures.

When she's not writing, Sierra enjoys spending time with her family, working in the world of advanced skincare and laser treatments, and creating content that educates and inspires others.

ABOUT THE ILLUSTRATOR

Farheen Fatima is a Canadian children's book illustrator who brings warmth, imagination, and charm to every page she creates. With a playful illustration style and a keen eye for detail, she transforms stories into engaging visual experiences that captivate young readers.

Passionate about visual storytelling, Farheen loves collaborating with authors and publishers to bring new tales to life through her artwork.

Ready to bring your story to life? Get in touch to discuss your project and create something children will treasure for years to come.

www.littlefolkstories.com

design@littlefolkstories.com

Scan to contact

www.ingramcontent.com/pod-product-compliance
Lightning Source LLC
LaVergne TN
LVHW071535210926
848349LV00013B/136

SUNNY the SKIN SHIELD

DEDICATION

To my sons-

You are the reason behind every page, every word, and every dream brought to life in this story. You are my heart, my inspiration, and the reason these stories came to life. Watching you grow, learn, and shine brighter each day is my greatest joy. This book - and the series to come - begins with you and was written with love that will last far beyond these pages.

To every child-

May this story be a reminder that you are strong, bright, and protected. This is just the beginning of a series made to help you grow with confidence, curiosity, and courage wherever life takes you.

Ryu loved to play outside in the warm, sunny air.
He ran, climbed, and laughed all day long.

His big brother, Dash, was always right beside him.
They were the best adventure team.

One morning Ryu said, "Do I have to wear sunscreen?"
He made a little scrunchy face.

Dash laughed and said, "You don't want to get burned!"
"Trust me I've learned the hard way."

That night, Ryu had a dream about his skin.
It looked like a strong, shiny castle.

Suddenly, ZAP! Bright sun rays came zooming down!
"Oh no!" Ryu shouted.

Then a glowing friend appeared.
"I'm Sunny the Shield! I protect your skin!"

Sunny covered the castle like a soft, shiny blanket.
The sun rays bounced right off, BOING!

"They can't get us?" Ryu asked.
"Not if you put sunscreen on every day!" Sunny said.

Ryu woke up with a big smile.
"Dash! We need sunscreen!"

The brothers put sunscreen on their faces, arms, and legs.
"We're protecting our castles!" they cheered.

Now Ryu and Dash wear sunscreen before every adventure.

PARENT PRO TIP
Find a Sunscreen with
Zinc Oxide & Titanium Dioxide
ZINC OXIDE
TITANIUM DIOXIDE
HARMFUL UV RAYS
SUNSCREEN LAYER
SKIN SURFACE
SKIN CELLS
DEEPER SKIN LAYERS
They sit on top of the skin and block harmful rays like a tiny shield.
Sunscreen should go on 15 minutes before sun exposure not right as you walk out the door.
Kids need more sunscreen than you think, about a full shot glass amount to cover the whole body.
"Waterproof" sunscreen isn't real. Look for water resistant and always reapply after swimming.
OCT 26
Sunscreen expires! Check the date. Old sunscreen can lose effectiveness.
Sprays are convenient, but lotions protect more evenly. (If using sprays rub them in after applying.)
LIP BALM SPF
Lips burn too – use a lip balm with SPF.
Most parents forget the sun is strongest between 10am-4pm even in cooler weather.
Protecting skin early is one of the easiest ways to prevent long term damage. Little steps now,
BIG PROTECTION FOR LIFE
SUNSCREEN SPF 50+

Pack Your Sun Safety Bag

Draw a line or circle to what belongs in your beach bag.

Sun Safety Word Search

Can you find all the hidden sun safety words?

HAT

SUN

SKIN

SAFE

SUNNY

WATER

SPF

SHADE

Y	U	N	Y	Y	V	O	F	O	G
S	U	N	N	Y	A	S	I	N	E
U	H	A	T	E	R	A	C	S	
N	O	I	D	H	E	F	B	P	
V	S	H	A	D	E	R	F		
W	K	T	T	R	O	H	A		
S	I	I	W	A	T	E	R		
S	N	N	Y	S	S	E	E		

Draw Yourself Having Fun in the Sun!

Can you draw yourself enjoying a sunny day?
Don't forget your sun safety gear!

Sun Safety Scavenger Hunt!

Look carefully! Find and circle each item below.

Sun	Shady tree	Hat
Sunglasses	Water bottle	Sunscreen

Color Sunny the Skin Shield!

Help Sunny Get to the Soccer Field

Connect the Dots!

Follow the numbers and discover WHAT THE SURPRISE IS

Match the Colors!

Can you match each color to the correct objects?

Circle the Things That Start with "S"

Can you find everything that begins with the letter S ?

Color by Numbers

Share your sunscreen with your buddy and color the picture with the relevant colors

Sun Safety

Write the correct words on the lines

1. Always wear a __________  when you are in the sun.

2. __________ 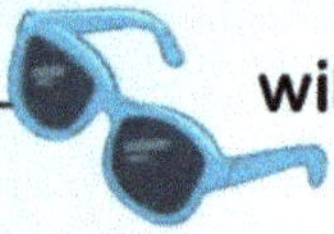 will help to protect your eyes from harmful rays of the sun.

3. Apply plenty of __________  to protect your skin from harmful rays.

4. After a few __________ 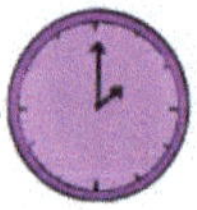 you need to reapply.

5. Cover your skin with a __________  if you can.

6. Play in the __________  for even better protection from the sun.

shade	hat	hours	sunscreen	shirt	sunglasses

ABOUT THE AUTHOR

Sierra Jeffress is a creative storyteller with a passion for bringing imagination to life through meaningful, engaging narratives. With a background in aesthetics and plastic surgery industry, she blends science, care, and creativity into everything she does.

Inspired by her love for children and storytelling, Sierra writes books that spark curiosity, build confidence, and make learning fun. Her work focuses on turning everyday lessons - like sun safety - into magical, memorable adventures.

When she's not writing, Sierra enjoys spending time with her family, working in the world of advanced skincare and laser treatments, and creating content that educates and inspires others.

ABOUT THE ILLUSTRATOR

Farheen Fatima is a Canadian children's book illustrator who brings warmth, imagination, and charm to every page she creates. With a playful illustration style and a keen eye for detail, she transforms stories into engaging visual experiences that captivate young readers.

Passionate about visual storytelling, Farheen loves collaborating with authors and publishers to bring new tales to life through her artwork.

Ready to bring your story to life? Get in touch to discuss your project and create something children will treasure for years to come.

www.littlefolkstories.com

design@littlefolkstories.com

Scan to contact

www.ingramcontent.com/pod-product-compliance
Lightning Source LLC
LaVergne TN
LVHW071535210926
848349LV00013B/136

* 9 7 9 8 2 3 4 1 0 3 7 5 8 *

SUNNY the SKIN SHIELD

DEDICATION

To my sons-

You are the reason behind every page, every word, and every dream brought to life in this story. You are my heart, my inspiration, and the reason these stories came to life. Watching you grow, learn, and shine brighter each day is my greatest joy. This book - and the series to come - begins with you and was written with love that will last far beyond these pages.

To every child-

May this story be a reminder that you are strong, bright, and protected. This is just the beginning of a series made to help you grow with confidence, curiosity, and courage wherever life takes you.

Ryu loved to play outside in the warm, sunny air.
He ran, climbed, and laughed all day long.

His big brother, Dash, was always right beside him.
They were the best adventure team.

One morning Ryu said, "Do I have to wear sunscreen?"
He made a little scrunchy face.

Dash laughed and said, "You don't want to get burned!"
"Trust me I've learned the hard way."

That night, Ryu had a dream about his skin.
It looked like a strong, shiny castle.

Suddenly, ZAP! Bright sun rays came zooming down!
"Oh no!" Ryu shouted.

Then a glowing friend appeared.
"I'm Sunny the Shield! I protect your skin!"

Sunny covered the castle like a soft, shiny blanket.
The sun rays bounced right off, BOING!

"They can't get us?" Ryu asked.
"Not if you put sunscreen on every day!" Sunny said.

Ryu woke up with a big smile.
"Dash! We need sunscreen!"

The brothers put sunscreen on their faces, arms, and legs.
"We're protecting our castles!" they cheered.

Now Ryu and Dash wear sunscreen before every adventure.

PARENT PRO TIP
Find a Sunscreen with
Zinc Oxide & Titanium Dioxide
ZINC OXIDE
TITANIUM DIOXIDE
HARMFUL UV RAYS
SUNSCREEN LAYER
SKIN SURFACE
SKIN CELLS
DEEPER SKIN LAYERS
They sit on top of the skin and block harmful rays like a tiny shield.
Sunscreen should go on 15 minutes before sun exposure not right as you walk out the door.
Kids need more sunscreen than you think, about a full shot glass amount to cover the whole body.
"Waterproof" sunscreen isn't real. Look for water resistant and always reapply after swimming.
OCT 26
Sunscreen expires! Check the date. Old sunscreen can lose effectiveness.
Sprays are convenient, but lotions protect more evenly. (if using sprays rub them in after applying.)
LIP BALM SPF
Lips burn too – use a lip balm with SPF.
Most parents forget the sun is strongest between 10am-4pm even in cooler weather.
SUNSCREEN SPF 50+
Protecting skin early is one of the easiest ways to prevent long term damage. Little steps now,
BIG PROTECTION FOR LIFE

Pack Your Sun Safety Bag

Draw a line or circle to what belongs in your beach bag.

Sun Safety Word Search

Can you find all the hidden sun safety words?

SUN

SKIN

SUNNY

SPF

HAT

SAFE

WATER

SHADE

Y U N Y Y V O F O G

S U N N Y A S I N E

U H A T E R A C S

N O I D H E F B P

V S H A D E R F

W K T T R O H A

S I I W A T E R

S N N Y S S E E

Draw Yourself Having Fun in the Sun!

Can you draw yourself enjoying a sunny day?
Don't forget your sun safety gear!

Sun Safety Scavenger Hunt!

Look carefully! Find and circle each item below.

Sun	Shady tree	Hat
Sunglasses	Water bottle	Sunscreen

Color Sunny the Skin Shield!

Help Sunny Get to the Soccer Field

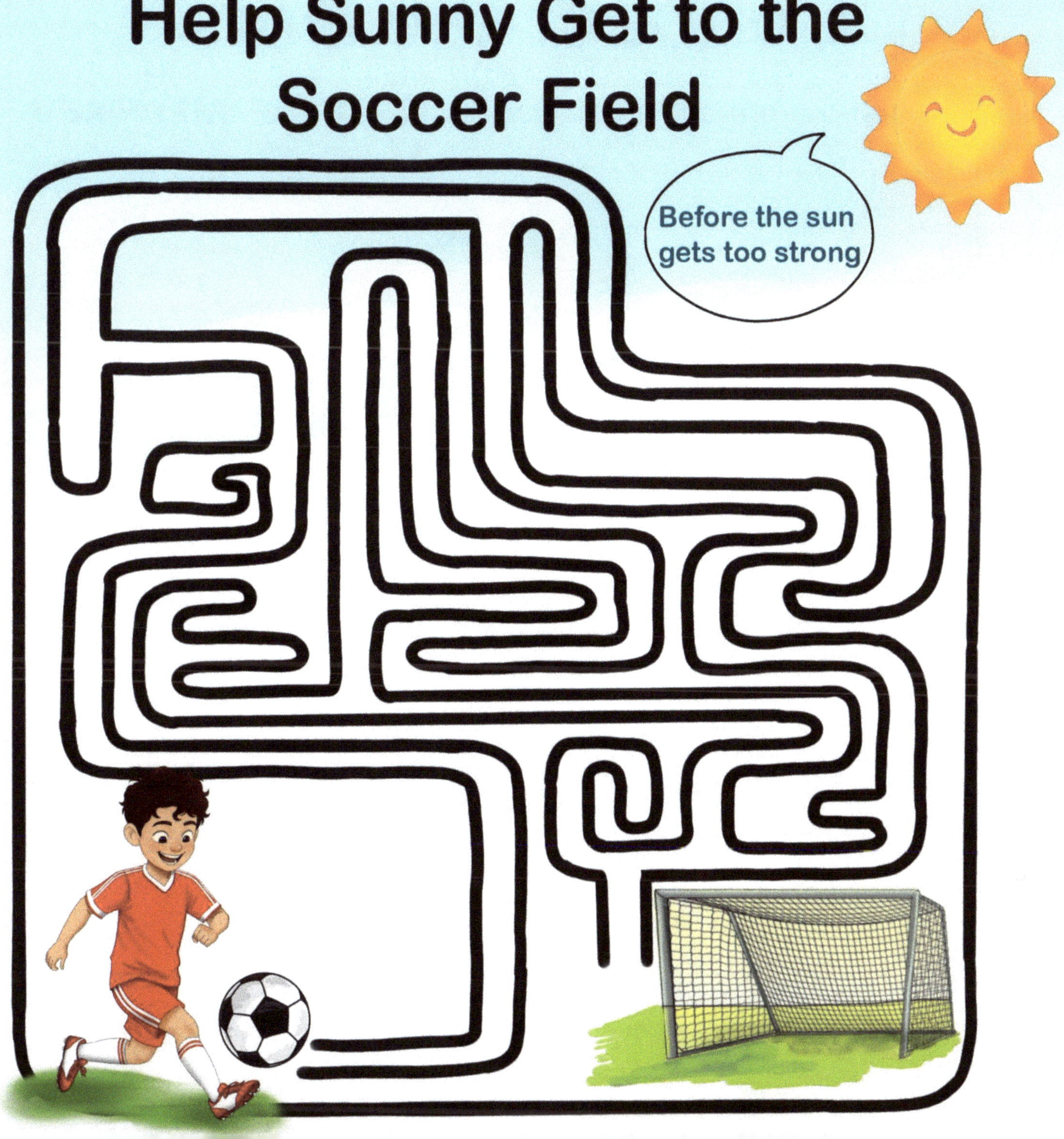

Connect the Dots!

Follow the numbers and discover WHAT THE SURPRISE IS

Match the Colors!

Can you match each color to the correct objects?

Circle the Things That Start with "S"

Can you find everything that begins with the letter S ?

Color by Numbers

Share your sunscreen with your buddy and color the picture with the relevant colors

Sun Safety

Write the correct words on the lines

1. Always wear a ____________  when you are in the sun.

2. ________________ 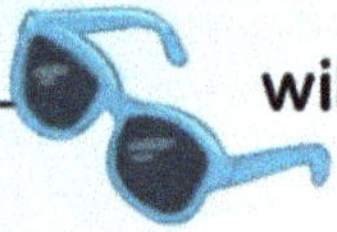 will help to protect your eyes from harmful rays of the sun.

3. Apply plenty of ________________  to protect your skin from harmful rays.

4. After a few ________________  you need to reapply.

5. Cover your skin with a ________________ 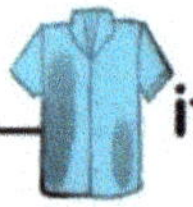 if you can.

6. Play in the ________________  for even better protection from the sun.

shade	hat	hours	sunscreen	shirt	sunglasses

ABOUT THE AUTHOR

Sierra Jeffress is a creative storyteller with a passion for bringing imagination to life through meaningful, engaging narratives. With a background in aesthetics and plastic surgery industry, she blends science, care, and creativity into everything she does.

Inspired by her love for children and storytelling, Sierra writes books that spark curiosity, build confidence, and make learning fun. Her work focuses on turning everyday lessons - like sun safety - into magical, memorable adventures.

When she's not writing, Sierra enjoys spending time with her family, working in the world of advanced skincare and laser treatments, and creating content that educates and inspires others.

ABOUT THE ILLUSTRATOR

Farheen Fatima is a Canadian children's book illustrator who brings warmth, imagination, and charm to every page she creates. With a playful illustration style and a keen eye for detail, she transforms stories into engaging visual experiences that captivate young readers.

Passionate about visual storytelling, Farheen loves collaborating with authors and publishers to bring new tales to life through her artwork.

Ready to bring your story to life? Get in touch to discuss your project and create something children will treasure for years to come.

www.littlefolkstories.com

design@littlefolkstories.com

Scan to contact

www.ingramcontent.com/pod-product-compliance
Lightning Source LLC
LaVergne TN
LVHW071535210926
848349LV00013B/136
* 9 7 9 8 2 3 4 1 0 3 7 5 8 *

DEDICATION

To my sons-

You are the reason behind every page, every word, and every dream brought to life in this story. You are my heart, my inspiration, and the reason these stories came to life. Watching you grow, learn, and shine brighter each day is my greatest joy. This book - and the series to come - begins with you and was written with love that will last far beyond these pages.

To every child-

May this story be a reminder that you are strong, bright, and protected. This is just the beginning of a series made to help you grow with confidence, curiosity, and courage wherever life takes you.

Ryu loved to play outside in the warm, sunny air.
He ran, climbed, and laughed all day long.

His big brother, Dash, was always right beside him.
They were the best adventure team.

One morning Ryu said, "Do I have to wear sunscreen?"
He made a little scrunchy face.

Dash laughed and said, "You don't want to get burned!"
"Trust me I've learned the hard way."

That night, Ryu had a dream about his skin.
It looked like a strong, shiny castle.

Suddenly, ZAP! Bright sun rays came zooming down!
"Oh no!" Ryu shouted.

Then a glowing friend appeared.
"I'm Sunny the Shield! I protect your skin!"

Sunny covered the castle like a soft, shiny blanket.
The sun rays bounced right off, BOING!

"They can't get us?" Ryu asked.
"Not if you put sunscreen on every day!" Sunny said.

Ryu woke up with a big smile.
"Dash! We need sunscreen!"

The brothers put sunscreen on their faces, arms, and legs.
"We're protecting our castles!" they cheered.

Now Ryu and Dash wear sunscreen before every adventure.

PARENT PRO TIP
Find a Sunscreen with
Zinc Oxide & Titanium Dioxide
ZINC OXIDE
TITANIUM DIOXIDE
HARMFUL UV RAYS
SUNSCREEN LAYER
SKIN SURFACE
SKIN CELLS
DEEPER SKIN LAYERS
They sit on top of the skin and block harmful rays like a tiny shield.
Sunscreen should go on 15 minutes before sun exposure not right as you walk out the door.
Kids need more sunscreen than you think, about a full shot glass amount to cover the whole body.
"Waterproof" sunscreen isn't real. Look for water resistant and always reapply after swimming.
OCT 26
Sunscreen expires! Check the date. Old sunscreen can lose effectiveness.
Sprays are convenient, but lotions protect more evenly. (if using sprays rub them in after applying.)
LIP BALM SPF
Lips burn too – use a lip balm with SPF.
Most parents forget the sun is strongest between 10am-4pm even in cooler weather.
SUNSCREEN SPF 50+
Protecting skin early is one of the easiest ways to prevent long term damage. Little steps now,
BIG PROTECTION FOR LIFE

Pack Your Sun Safety Bag

Draw a line or circle to what belongs in your beach bag.

Sun Safety Word Search

Can you find all the hidden sun safety words?

SUN

SKIN

SUNNY

SPF

HAT

SAFE

WATER

SHADE

Y U N Y Y V O F O G
S U N N Y A S I N E
U H A T E R A C S
N O I D H E F B P
V S H A D E R F
W K T T R O H A
S I I W A T E R
S N N Y S S E E

Draw Yourself Having Fun in the Sun!

Can you draw yourself enjoying a sunny day?
Don't forget your sun safety gear!

Sun Safety Scavenger Hunt!

Look carefully! Find and circle each item below.

Sun	Shady tree	Hat
Sunglasses	Water bottle	Sunscreen

Color Sunny the Skin Shield!

Help Sunny Get to the Soccer Field

Connect the Dots!

Follow the numbers and discover WHAT THE SURPRISE IS

Match the Colors!

Can you match each color to the correct objects?

Circle the Things That Start with “S”

Can you find everything that begins with the letter S ?

Color by Numbers

Share your sunscreen with your buddy and color the picture with the relevant colors

Sun Safety

Write the correct words on the lines

1. Always wear a __________  when you are in the sun.

2. __________  will help to protect your eyes from harmful rays of the sun.

3. Apply plenty of __________ 

to protect your skin from harmful rays.

4. After a few __________ 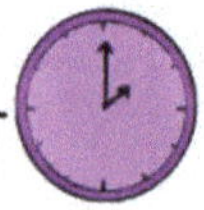 you need to reapply.

5. Cover your skin with a __________ 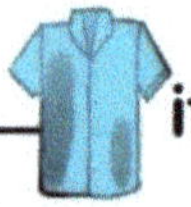 if you can.

6. Play in the __________  for even better protection from the sun.

shade	hat	hours	sunscreen	shirt	sunglasses

ABOUT THE AUTHOR

Sierra Jeffress is a creative storyteller with a passion for bringing imagination to life through meaningful, engaging narratives. With a background in aesthetics and plastic surgery industry, she blends science, care, and creativity into everything she does.

Inspired by her love for children and storytelling, Sierra writes books that spark curiosity, build confidence, and make learning fun. Her work focuses on turning everyday lessons - like sun safety - into magical, memorable adventures.

When she's not writing, Sierra enjoys spending time with her family, working in the world of advanced skincare and laser treatments, and creating content that educates and inspires others.

ABOUT THE ILLUSTRATOR

Farheen Fatima is a Canadian children's book illustrator who brings warmth, imagination, and charm to every page she creates. With a playful illustration style and a keen eye for detail, she transforms stories into engaging visual experiences that captivate young readers.

Passionate about visual storytelling, Farheen loves collaborating with authors and publishers to bring new tales to life through her artwork.

Ready to bring your story to life? Get in touch to discuss your project and create something children will treasure for years to come.

www.littlefolkstories.com

design@littlefolkstories.com

Scan to contact

www.ingramcontent.com/pod-product-compliance
Lightning Source LLC
LaVergne TN
LVHW071535210926
848349LV00013B/136

SUNNY the SKIN SHIELD

DEDICATION

To my sons-
You are the reason behind every page, every word, and every dream brought to life in this story. You are my heart, my inspiration, and the reason these stories came to life. Watching you grow, learn, and shine brighter each day is my greatest joy. This book - and the series to come - begins with you and was written with love that will last far beyond these pages.

To every child-
May this story be a reminder that you are strong, bright, and protected. This is just the beginning of a series made to help you grow with confidence, curiosity, and courage wherever life takes you.

Ryu loved to play outside in the warm, sunny air.
He ran, climbed, and laughed all day long.

His big brother, Dash, was always right beside him.
They were the best adventure team.

One morning Ryu said, "Do I have to wear sunscreen?"
He made a little scrunchy face.

Dash laughed and said, "You don't want to get burned!"
"Trust me I've learned the hard way."

That night, Ryu had a dream about his skin.
It looked like a strong, shiny castle.

Suddenly, ZAP! Bright sun rays came zooming down!
"Oh no!" Ryu shouted.

Then a glowing friend appeared.
"I'm Sunny the Shield! I protect your skin!"

Sunny covered the castle like a soft, shiny blanket.
The sun rays bounced right off, BOING!

"They can't get us?" Ryu asked.
"Not if you put sunscreen on every day!" Sunny said.

Ryu woke up with a big smile.
"Dash! We need sunscreen!"

The brothers put sunscreen on their faces, arms, and legs.
"We're protecting our castles!" they cheered.

Now Ryu and Dash wear sunscreen before every adventure.

PARENT PRO TIP

Find a Sunscreen with Zinc Oxide & Titanium Dioxide

- Sunscreen should go on 15 minutes before sun exposure not right as you walk out the door.
- Kids need more sunscreen than you think, about a full shot glass amount to cover the whole body.
- "Waterproof" sunscreen isn't real. Look for water resistant and always reapply after swimming.
- OCT 26 — Sunscreen expires! Check the date. Old sunscreen can lose effectiveness.
- Sprays are convenient, but lotions protect more evenly. (If using sprays rub them in after applying.)
- LIP BALM SPF — Lips burn too – use a lip balm with SPF.
- Most parents forget the sun is strongest between 10am-4pm even in cooler weather.

Protecting skin early is one of the easiest ways to prevent long term damage. Little steps now,

BIG PROTECTION FOR LIFE

Pack Your Sun Safety Bag

Draw a line or circle to what belongs in your beach bag.

Sun Safety Word Search

Can you find all the hidden sun safety words?

Y U N Y Y V O F O G
S U N N Y A S I N E
U H A T E R A C S
N O I D H E F B P
V S H A D E R F
W K T T R O H A
S I I W A T E R
S N N Y S S E E

SUN
SKIN
SUNNY
SPF
HAT
SAFE
WATER
SHADE

Draw Yourself Having Fun in the Sun!

Can you draw yourself enjoying a sunny day?
Don't forget your sun safety gear!

Sun Safety Scavenger Hunt!

Look carefully! Find and circle each item below.

Sun	Shady tree	Hat
Sunglasses	Water bottle	Sunscreen

Color Sunny the Skin Shield!

Help Sunny Get to the Soccer Field

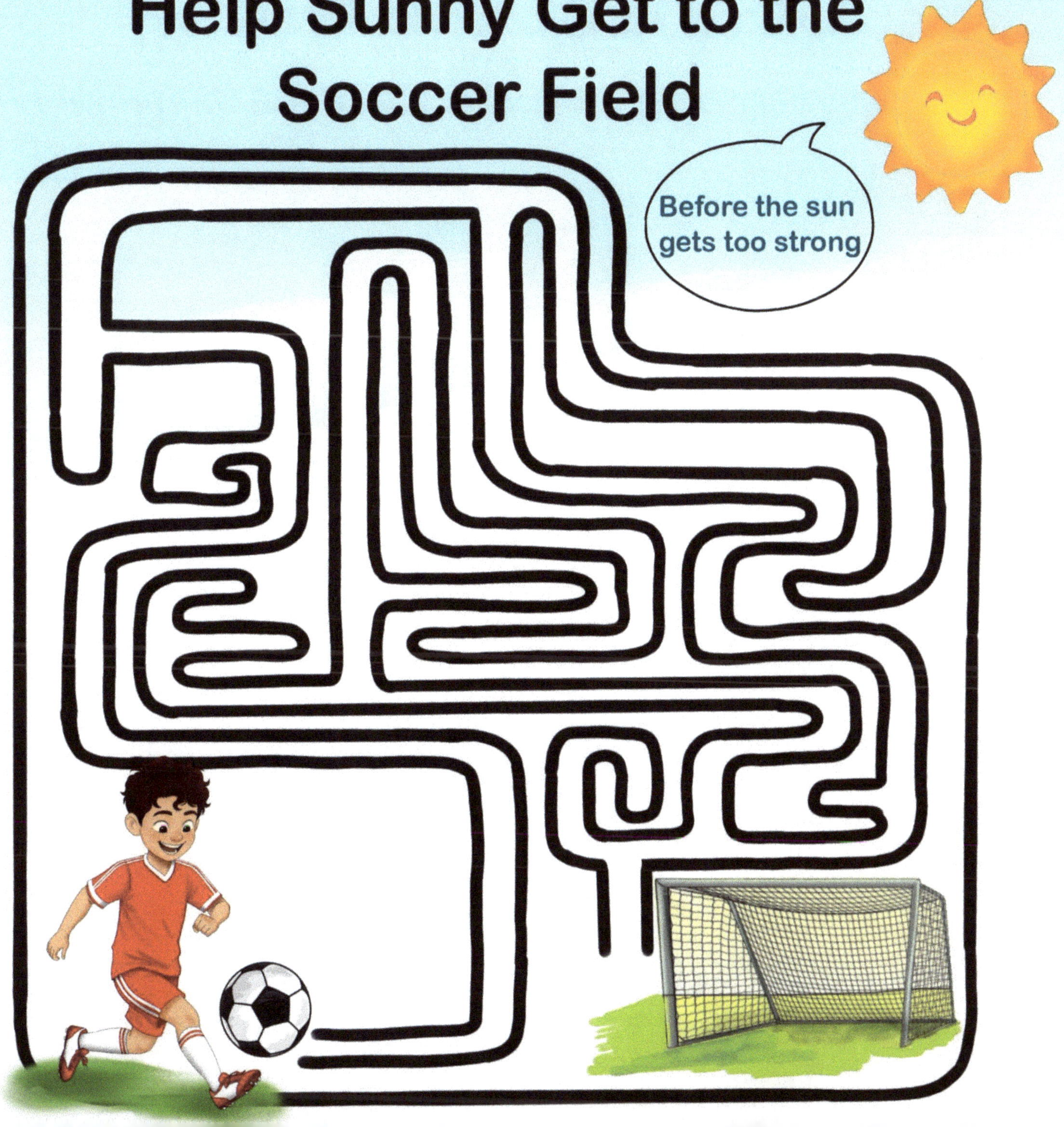

Connect the Dots!

Follow the numbers and discover WHAT THE SURPRISE IS

Match the Colors!

Can you match each color to the correct objects?

Circle the Things That Start with "S"

Can you find everything that begins with the letter S ?

Color by Numbers

Share your sunscreen with your buddy and color the picture with the relevant colors

Sun Safety

Write the correct words on the lines

1. Always wear a __________  when you are in the sun.

2. __________  will help to protect your eyes from harmful rays of the sun.

3. Apply plenty of __________  to protect your skin from harmful rays.

4. After a few __________  you need to reapply.

5. Cover your skin with a __________ 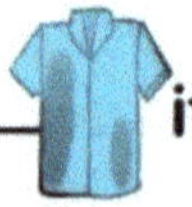 if you can.

6. Play in the __________  for even better protection from the sun.

shade	hat	hours	sunscreen	shirt	sunglasses

ABOUT THE AUTHOR

Sierra Jeffress is a creative storyteller with a passion for bringing imagination to life through meaningful, engaging narratives. With a background in aesthetics and plastic surgery industry, she blends science, care, and creativity into everything she does.

Inspired by her love for children and storytelling, Sierra writes books that spark curiosity, build confidence, and make learning fun. Her work focuses on turning everyday lessons - like sun safety - into magical, memorable adventures.

When she's not writing, Sierra enjoys spending time with her family, working in the world of advanced skincare and laser treatments, and creating content that educates and inspires others.

ABOUT THE ILLUSTRATOR

Farheen Fatima is a Canadian children's book illustrator who brings warmth, imagination, and charm to every page she creates. With a playful illustration style and a keen eye for detail, she transforms stories into engaging visual experiences that captivate young readers.

Passionate about visual storytelling, Farheen loves collaborating with authors and publishers to bring new tales to life through her artwork.

Ready to bring your story to life? Get in touch to discuss your project and create something children will treasure for years to come.

www.littlefolkstories.com

design@littlefolkstories.com

Scan to contact

www.ingramcontent.com/pod-product-compliance
Lightning Source LLC
LaVergne TN
LVHW071535210926
848349LV00013B/136

SUNNY the SKIN SHIELD

DEDICATION

To my sons-

You are the reason behind every page, every word, and every dream brought to life in this story. You are my heart, my inspiration, and the reason these stories came to life. Watching you grow, learn, and shine brighter each day is my greatest joy. This book - and the series to come - begins with you and was written with love that will last far beyond these pages.

To every child-

May this story be a reminder that you are strong, bright, and protected. This is just the beginning of a series made to help you grow with confidence, curiosity, and courage wherever life takes you.

Ryu loved to play outside in the warm, sunny air.
He ran, climbed, and laughed all day long.

His big brother, Dash, was always right beside him. They were the best adventure team.

One morning Ryu said, "Do I have to wear sunscreen?"
He made a little scrunchy face.

Dash laughed and said, "You don't want to get burned!"
"Trust me I've learned the hard way."

That night, Ryu had a dream about his skin.
It looked like a strong, shiny castle.

Suddenly, ZAP! Bright sun rays came zooming down!
"Oh no!" Ryu shouted.

Then a glowing friend appeared.
"I'm Sunny the Shield! I protect your skin!"

Sunny covered the castle like a soft, shiny blanket.
The sun rays bounced right off, BOING!

"They can't get us?" Ryu asked.
"Not if you put sunscreen on every day!" Sunny said.

Ryu woke up with a big smile.
"Dash! We need sunscreen!"

The brothers put sunscreen on their faces, arms, and legs.
"We're protecting our castles!" they cheered.

Now Ryu and Dash wear sunscreen before every adventure.

PARENT PRO TIP
Find a Sunscreen with
Zinc Oxide & Titanium Dioxide
ZINC OXIDE
TITANIUM DIOXIDE
HARMFUL UV RAYS
SUNSCREEN LAYER
SKIN SURFACE
SKIN CELLS
DEEPER SKIN LAYERS
They sit on top of the skin and block harmful rays like a tiny shield.
Sunscreen should go on 15 minutes before sun exposure not right as you walk out the door.
Kids need more sunscreen than you think, about a full shot glass amount to cover the whole body.
"Waterproof" sunscreen isn't real. Look for water resistant and always reapply after swimming.
OCT 26
Sunscreen expires! Check the date. Old sunscreen can lose effectiveness.
Sprays are convenient, but lotions protect more evenly. (If using sprays rub them in after applying.)
LIP BALM SPF
Lips burn too – use a lip balm with SPF.
Most parents forget the sun is strongest between 10am-4pm even in cooler weather.
SUNSCREEN SPF 50+
Protecting skin early is one of the easiest ways to prevent long term damage. Little steps now,
BIG PROTECTION FOR LIFE

Pack Your Sun Safety Bag

Draw a line or circle to what belongs in your beach bag.

Sun Safety Word Search

Can you find all the hidden sun safety words?

Y U N Y Y V O F O G
S U N N Y A S I N E
U H A T E R A C S
N O I D H E F B P
V S H A D E R F
W K T T R O H A
S I I W A T E R
S N N Y S S E E

- HAT
- SUN
- SKIN
- SAFE
- SUNNY
- WATER
- SPF
- SHADE

Draw Yourself Having Fun in the Sun!

Can you draw yourself enjoying a sunny day?
Don’t forget your sun safety gear!

Sun Safety Scavenger Hunt!

Look carefully! Find and circle each item below.

Sun	Shady tree	Hat
Sunglasses	Water bottle	Sunscreen

Color Sunny the Skin Shield!

Help Sunny Get to the Soccer Field

Connect the Dots!

Follow the numbers and discover WHAT THE SURPRISE IS

Match the Colors!

Can you match each color to the correct objects?

Circle the Things That Start with "S"

Can you find everything that begins with the letter S ?

Color by Numbers

Share your sunscreen with your buddy and color the picture with the relevant colors

1 2 3 4 5 6 7 8 9

Sun Safety

Write the correct words on the lines

1. Always wear a __________  when you are in the sun.

2. __________  will help to protect your eyes from harmful rays of the sun.

3. Apply plenty of __________ 

to protect your skin from harmful rays.

4. After a few __________ 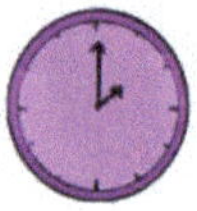 you need to reapply.

5. Cover your skin with a __________ 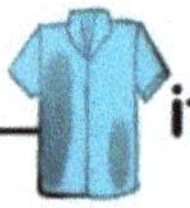 if you can.

6. Play in the __________  for even better protection from the sun.

shade	hat	hours	sunscreen	shirt	sunglasses

ABOUT THE AUTHOR

Sierra Jeffress is a creative storyteller with a passion for bringing imagination to life through meaningful, engaging narratives. With a background in aesthetics and plastic surgery industry, she blends science, care, and creativity into everything she does.

Inspired by her love for children and storytelling, Sierra writes books that spark curiosity, build confidence, and make learning fun. Her work focuses on turning everyday lessons - like sun safety - into magical, memorable adventures.

When she's not writing, Sierra enjoys spending time with her family, working in the world of advanced skincare and laser treatments, and creating content that educates and inspires others.

ABOUT THE ILLUSTRATOR

Farheen Fatima is a Canadian children's book illustrator who brings warmth, imagination, and charm to every page she creates. With a playful illustration style and a keen eye for detail, she transforms stories into engaging visual experiences that captivate young readers.

Passionate about visual storytelling, Farheen loves collaborating with authors and publishers to bring new tales to life through her artwork.

Ready to bring your story to life? Get in touch to discuss your project and create something children will treasure for years to come.

www.littlefolkstories.com

design@littlefolkstories.com

Scan to contact

www.ingramcontent.com/pod-product-compliance
Lightning Source LLC
LaVergne TN
LVHW071535210926
848349LV00013B/136

DEDICATION

To my sons-

You are the reason behind every page, every word, and every dream brought to life in this story. You are my heart, my inspiration, and the reason these stories came to life. Watching you grow, learn, and shine brighter each day is my greatest joy. This book - and the series to come - begins with you and was written with love that will last far beyond these pages.

To every child-

May this story be a reminder that you are strong, bright, and protected. This is just the beginning of a series made to help you grow with confidence, curiosity, and courage wherever life takes you.

Ryu loved to play outside in the warm, sunny air.
He ran, climbed, and laughed all day long.

His big brother, Dash, was always right beside him.
They were the best adventure team.

One morning Ryu said, "Do I have to wear sunscreen?"
He made a little scrunchy face.

Dash laughed and said, "You don't want to get burned!"
"Trust me I've learned the hard way."

That night, Ryu had a dream about his skin.
It looked like a strong, shiny castle.

Suddenly, ZAP! Bright sun rays came zooming down!
"Oh no!" Ryu shouted.

Then a glowing friend appeared.
"I'm Sunny the Shield! I protect your skin!"

Sunny covered the castle like a soft, shiny blanket.
The sun rays bounced right off, BOING!

"They can't get us?" Ryu asked.
"Not if you put sunscreen on every day!" Sunny said.

Ryu woke up with a big smile.
"Dash! We need sunscreen!"

The brothers put sunscreen on their faces, arms, and legs. "We're protecting our castles!" they cheered.

Now Ryu and Dash wear sunscreen before every adventure.

PARENT PRO TIP
Find a Sunscreen with
Zinc Oxide & Titanium Dioxide
ZINC OXIDE
TITANIUM DIOXIDE
HARMFUL UV RAYS
SUNSCREEN LAYER
SKIN SURFACE
SKIN CELLS
DEEPER SKIN LAYERS
They sit on top of the skin and block harmful rays like a tiny shield.
Sunscreen should go on 15 minutes before sun exposure not right as you walk out the door.
Kids need more sunscreen than you think, about a full shot glass amount to cover the whole body.
"Waterproof" sunscreen isn't real. Look for water resistant and always reapply after swimming.
OCT 26
Sunscreen expires! Check the date. Old sunscreen can lose effectiveness.
Sprays are convenient, but lotions protect more evenly. (If using sprays rub them in after applying.)
LIP BALM SPF
Lips burn too – use a lip balm with SPF.
Most parents forget the sun is strongest between 10am-4pm even in cooler weather.
SUNSCREEN SPF 50+
Protecting skin early is one of the easiest ways to prevent long term damage. Little steps now,
BIG PROTECTION FOR LIFE

Pack Your Sun Safety Bag

Draw a line or circle to what belongs in your beach bag.

Sun Safety Word Search

Can you find all the hidden sun safety words?

Y U N Y Y V O F O G
S U N N Y A S I N E
U H A T E R A C S
N O I D H E F B P
V S H A D E R F
W K T T R O H A
S I I W A T E R
S N N Y S S E E

HAT
SUN
SKIN
SAFE
SUNNY
WATER
SPF
SHADE

Draw Yourself Having Fun in the Sun!

Can you draw yourself enjoying a sunny day?
Don't forget your sun safety gear!

Sun Safety Scavenger Hunt!

Look carefully! Find and circle each item below.

Sun	Shady tree	Hat
Sunglasses	Water bottle	Sunscreen

Color Sunny the Skin Shield!

Help Sunny Get to the Soccer Field

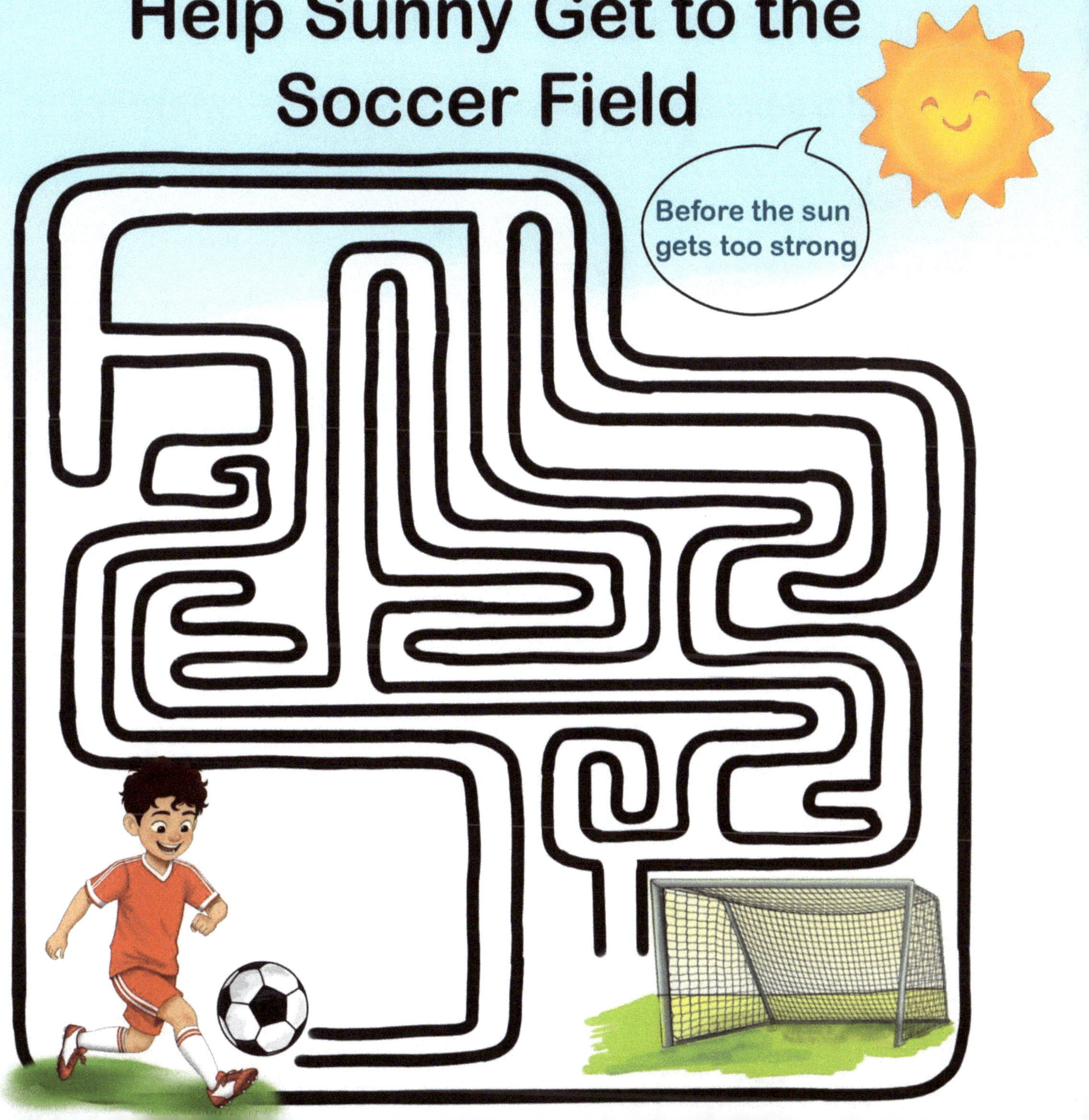

Connect the Dots!

Follow the numbers and discover WHAT THE SURPRISE IS

Match the Colors!

Can you match each color to the correct objects?

Circle the Things That Start with "S"

Can you find everything that begins with the letter S ?

Color by Numbers

Share your sunscreen with your buddy and color the picture with the relevant colors

Sun Safety

Write the correct words on the lines

1. Always wear a __________  when you are in the sun.

2. __________  will help to protect your eyes from harmful rays of the sun.

3. Apply plenty of __________  to protect your skin from harmful rays.

4. After a few __________  you need to reapply.

5. Cover your skin with a __________ 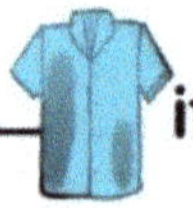 if you can.

6. Play in the __________  for even better protection from the sun.

shade	hat	hours	sunscreen	shirt	sunglasses

ABOUT THE AUTHOR

Sierra Jeffress is a creative storyteller with a passion for bringing imagination to life through meaningful, engaging narratives. With a background in aesthetics and plastic surgery industry, she blends science, care, and creativity into everything she does.

Inspired by her love for children and storytelling, Sierra writes books that spark curiosity, build confidence, and make learning fun. Her work focuses on turning everyday lessons - like sun safety - into magical, memorable adventures.

When she's not writing, Sierra enjoys spending time with her family, working in the world of advanced skincare and laser treatments, and creating content that educates and inspires others.

ABOUT THE ILLUSTRATOR

Farheen Fatima is a Canadian children's book illustrator who brings warmth, imagination, and charm to every page she creates. With a playful illustration style and a keen eye for detail, she transforms stories into engaging visual experiences that captivate young readers.

Passionate about visual storytelling, Farheen loves collaborating with authors and publishers to bring new tales to life through her artwork.

Ready to bring your story to life? Get in touch to discuss your project and create something children will treasure for years to come.

www.littlefolkstories.com

design@littlefolkstories.com

Scan to contact

www.ingramcontent.com/pod-product-compliance
Lightning Source LLC
LaVergne TN
LVHW071535210926
848349LV00013B/136
* 9 7 9 8 2 3 4 1 0 3 7 5 8 *

DEDICATION

To my sons-
You are the reason behind every page, every word, and every dream brought to life in this story. You are my heart, my inspiration, and the reason these stories came to life. Watching you grow, learn, and shine brighter each day is my greatest joy. This book - and the series to come - begins with you and was written with love that will last far beyond these pages.

To every child-
May this story be a reminder that you are strong, bright, and protected. This is just the beginning of a series made to help you grow with confidence, curiosity, and courage wherever life takes you.

Ryu loved to play outside in the warm, sunny air.
He ran, climbed, and laughed all day long.

His big brother, Dash, was always right beside him.
They were the best adventure team.

One morning Ryu said, "Do I have to wear sunscreen?"
He made a little scrunchy face.

Dash laughed and said, "You don't want to get burned!"
"Trust me I've learned the hard way."

That night, Ryu had a dream about his skin.
It looked like a strong, shiny castle.

Suddenly, ZAP! Bright sun rays came zooming down!
"Oh no!" Ryu shouted.

Then a glowing friend appeared.
"I'm Sunny the Shield! I protect your skin!"

Sunny covered the castle like a soft, shiny blanket.
The sun rays bounced right off, BOING!

"They can't get us?" Ryu asked.
"Not if you put sunscreen on every day!" Sunny said.

Ryu woke up with a big smile.
"Dash! We need sunscreen!"

The brothers put sunscreen on their faces, arms, and legs.
"We're protecting our castles!" they cheered.

Now Ryu and Dash wear sunscreen before every adventure.

PARENT PRO TIP
Find a Sunscreen with Zinc Oxide & Titanium Dioxide
ZINC OXIDE
TITANIUM DIOXIDE
HARMFUL UV RAYS
SUNSCREEN LAYER
SKIN SURFACE
SKIN CELLS
DEEPER SKIN LAYERS
They sit on top of the skin and block harmful rays like a tiny shield.
Sunscreen should go on 15 minutes before sun exposure not right as you walk out the door.
Kids need more sunscreen than you think, about a full shot glass amount to cover the whole body.
"Waterproof" sunscreen isn't real. Look for water resistant and always reapply after swimming.
OCT 26
Sunscreen expires! Check the date. Old sunscreen can lose effectiveness.
Sprays are convenient, but lotions protect more evenly. (If using sprays rub them in after applying.)
LIP BALM SPF
Lips burn too – use a lip balm with SPF.
Most parents forget the sun is strongest between 10am-4pm even in cooler weather.
SUNSCREEN SPF 50+
Protecting skin early is one of the easiest ways to prevent long term damage. Little steps now,
BIG PROTECTION FOR LIFE

Pack Your Sun Safety Bag

Draw a line or circle to what belongs in your beach bag.

Sun Safety Word Search

Can you find all the hidden sun safety words?

HAT

SUN

SKIN

SAFE

SUNNY

WATER

SPF

SHADE

Y U N Y Y V O F O G
S U N N Y A S I N E
U H A T E R A C S
N O I D H E F B P
V S H A D E R F
W K T T R O H A
S I I W A T E R
S N N Y S S E E

Draw Yourself Having Fun in the Sun!

Can you draw yourself enjoying a sunny day?
Don't forget your sun safety gear!

Sun Safety Scavenger Hunt!

Look carefully! Find and circle each item below.

Sun	Shady tree	Hat
Sunglasses	Water bottle	Sunscreen

Color Sunny the Skin Shield!

Help Sunny Get to the Soccer Field

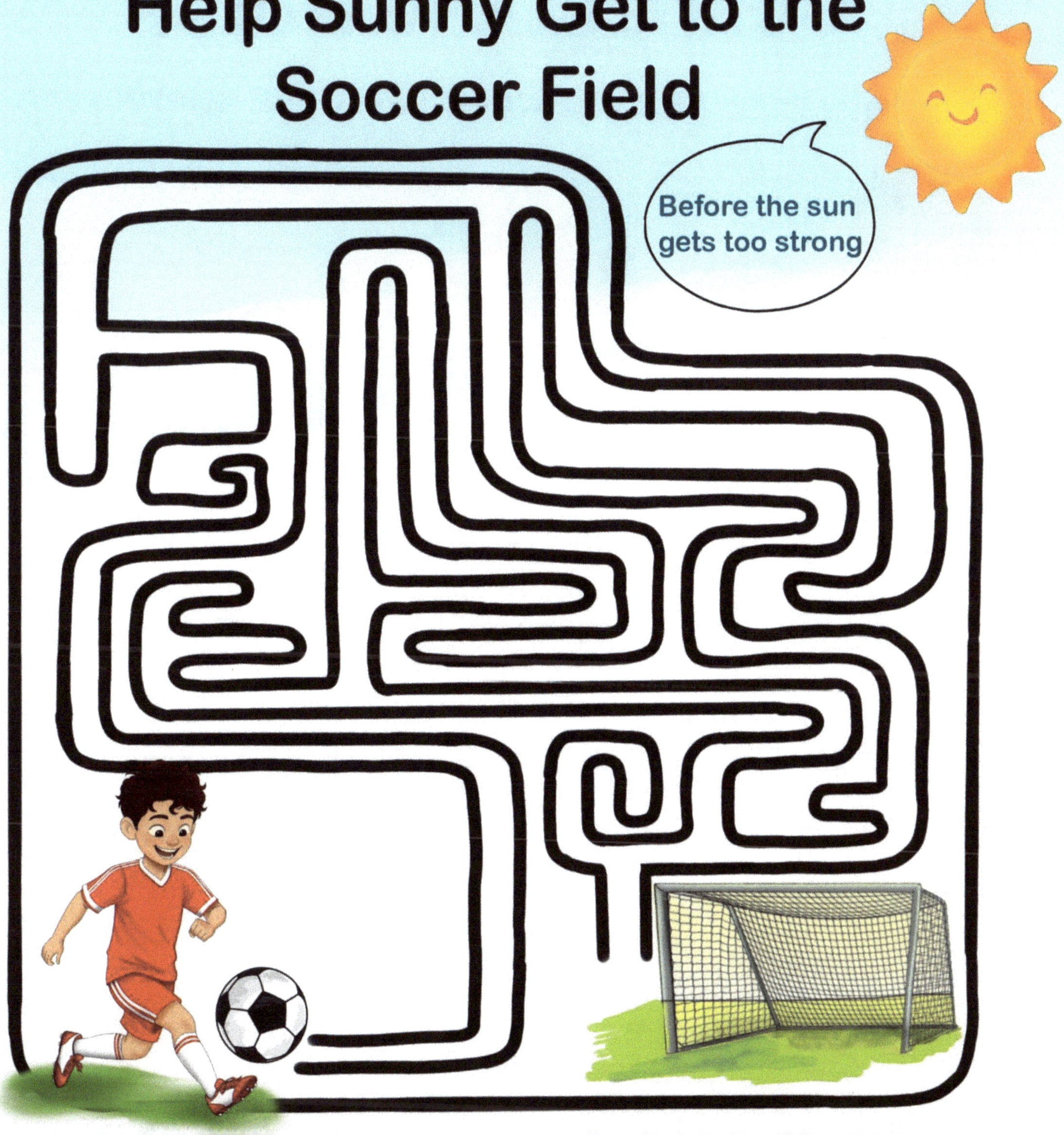

Connect the Dots!

Follow the numbers and discover WHAT THE SURPRISE IS

Match the Colors!

Can you match each color to the correct objects?

Circle the Things That Start with "S"

Can you find everything that begins with the letter S ?

Color by Numbers

Share your sunscreen with your buddy and color the picture with the relevant colors

1 2 3 4 5 6 7 8 9

Sun Safety

Write the correct words on the lines

1. Always wear a ____________  when you are in the sun.

2. ____________ 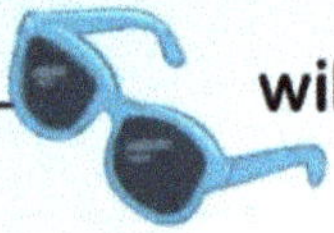 will help to protect your eyes from harmful rays of the sun.

3. Apply plenty of ____________  to protect your skin from harmful rays.

4. After a few ____________  you need to reapply.

5. Cover your skin with a ____________  if you can.

6. Play in the ____________  for even better protection from the sun.

shade	hat	hours	sunscreen	shirt	sunglasses

ABOUT THE AUTHOR

Sierra Jeffress is a creative storyteller with a passion for bringing imagination to life through meaningful, engaging narratives. With a background in aesthetics and plastic surgery industry, she blends science, care, and creativity into everything she does.

Inspired by her love for children and storytelling, Sierra writes books that spark curiosity, build confidence, and make learning fun. Her work focuses on turning everyday lessons - like sun safety - into magical, memorable adventures.

When she's not writing, Sierra enjoys spending time with her family, working in the world of advanced skincare and laser treatments, and creating content that educates and inspires others.

ABOUT THE ILLUSTRATOR

Farheen Fatima is a Canadian children's book illustrator who brings warmth, imagination, and charm to every page she creates. With a playful illustration style and a keen eye for detail, she transforms stories into engaging visual experiences that captivate young readers.

Passionate about visual storytelling, Farheen loves collaborating with authors and publishers to bring new tales to life through her artwork.

Ready to bring your story to life? Get in touch to discuss your project and create something children will treasure for years to come.

www.littlefolkstories.com

design@littlefolkstories.com

Scan to contact

www.ingramcontent.com/pod-product-compliance
Lightning Source LLC
LaVergne TN
LVHW071535210926
848349LV00013B/136
* 9 7 9 8 2 3 4 1 0 3 7 5 8 *

DEDICATION

To my sons-

You are the reason behind every page, every word, and every dream brought to life in this story. You are my heart, my inspiration, and the reason these stories came to life. Watching you grow, learn, and shine brighter each day is my greatest joy. This book - and the series to come - begins with you and was written with love that will last far beyond these pages.

To every child-

May this story be a reminder that you are strong, bright, and protected. This is just the beginning of a series made to help you grow with confidence, curiosity, and courage wherever life takes you.

Ryu loved to play outside in the warm, sunny air.
He ran, climbed, and laughed all day long.

His big brother, Dash, was always right beside him.
They were the best adventure team.

One morning Ryu said, "Do I have to wear sunscreen?"
He made a little scrunchy face.

Dash laughed and said, "You don't want to get burned!"
"Trust me I've learned the hard way."

That night, Ryu had a dream about his skin.
It looked like a strong, shiny castle.

Suddenly, ZAP! Bright sun rays came zooming down!
"Oh no!" Ryu shouted.

Then a glowing friend appeared.
"I'm Sunny the Shield! I protect your skin!"

Sunny covered the castle like a soft, shiny blanket.
The sun rays bounced right off, BOING!

"They can't get us?" Ryu asked.
"Not if you put sunscreen on every day!" Sunny said.

Ryu woke up with a big smile.
"Dash! We need sunscreen!"

The brothers put sunscreen on their faces, arms, and legs.
"We're protecting our castles!" they cheered.

Now Ryu and Dash wear sunscreen before every adventure.

PARENT PRO TIP

Find a Sunscreen with Zinc Oxide & Titanium Dioxide

- Sunscreen should go on 15 minutes before sun exposure not right as you walk out the door.
- Kids need more sunscreen than you think, about a full shot glass amount to cover the whole body.
- "Waterproof" sunscreen isn't real. Look for water resistant and always reapply after swimming.
- OCT 26 — Sunscreen expires! Check the date. Old sunscreen can lose effectiveness.
- Sprays are convenient, but lotions protect more evenly. (If using sprays rub them in after applying.)
- LIP BALM SPF — Lips burn too – use a lip balm with SPF.
- Most parents forget the sun is strongest between 10am-4pm even in cooler weather.

Protecting skin early is one of the easiest ways to prevent long term damage. Little steps now,

BIG PROTECTION FOR LIFE

SUNSCREEN SPF 50+

Pack Your Sun Safety Bag

Draw a line or circle to what belongs in your beach bag.

Sun Safety Word Search

Can you find all the hidden sun safety words?

HAT

SUN

SKIN

SAFE

SUNNY

WATER

SPF

SHADE

Y	U	N	Y	Y	V	O	F	O	G
S	U	N	N	Y	A	S	I	N	E
U	H	A	T	E	R	A	C	S	
N	O	I	D	H	E	F	B	P	
V	S	H	A	D	E	R	F		
W	K	T	T	R	O	H	A		
S	I	I	W	A	T	E	R		
S	N	N	Y	S	S	E	E		

Draw Yourself Having Fun in the Sun!

Can you draw yourself enjoying a sunny day?
Don't forget your sun safety gear!

Sun Safety Scavenger Hunt!

Look carefully! Find and circle each item below.

Sun	Shady tree	Hat
Sunglasses	Water bottle	Sunscreen

Color Sunny the Skin Shield!

Help Sunny Get to the Soccer Field

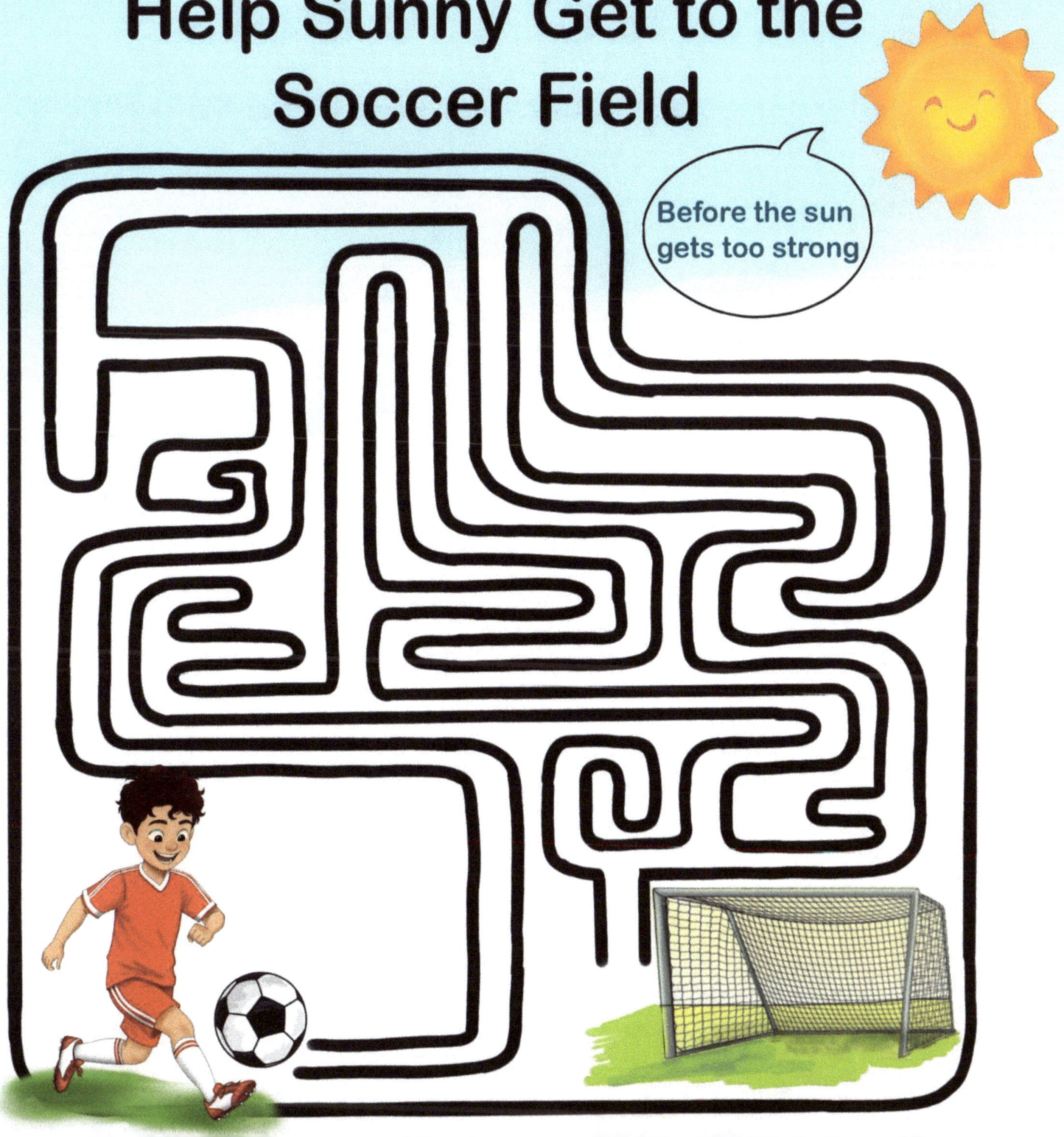

Connect the Dots!

Follow the numbers and discover WHAT THE SURPRISE IS

Match the Colors!

Can you match each color to the correct objects?

Circle the Things That Start with "S"

Can you find everything that begins with the letter S ?

Color by Numbers

Share your sunscreen with your buddy and color the picture with the relevant colors

Sun Safety

Write the correct words on the lines

1. Always wear a __________  when you are in the sun.

2. __________  will help to protect your eyes from harmful rays of the sun.

3. Apply plenty of __________  to protect your skin from harmful rays.

4. After a few __________  you need to reapply.

5. Cover your skin with a __________ 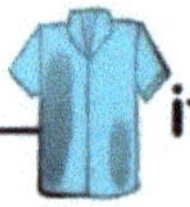 if you can.

6. Play in the __________  for even better protection from the sun.

shade	hat	hours	sunscreen	shirt	sunglasses

ABOUT THE AUTHOR

Sierra Jeffress is a creative storyteller with a passion for bringing imagination to life through meaningful, engaging narratives. With a background in aesthetics and plastic surgery industry, she blends science, care, and creativity into everything she does.

Inspired by her love for children and storytelling, Sierra writes books that spark curiosity, build confidence, and make learning fun. Her work focuses on turning everyday lessons - like sun safety - into magical, memorable adventures.

When she's not writing, Sierra enjoys spending time with her family, working in the world of advanced skincare and laser treatments, and creating content that educates and inspires others.

ABOUT THE ILLUSTRATOR

Farheen Fatima is a Canadian children's book illustrator who brings warmth, imagination, and charm to every page she creates. With a playful illustration style and a keen eye for detail, she transforms stories into engaging visual experiences that captivate young readers.

Passionate about visual storytelling, Farheen loves collaborating with authors and publishers to bring new tales to life through her artwork.

Ready to bring your story to life? Get in touch to discuss your project and create something children will treasure for years to come.

www.littlefolkstories.com

design@littlefolkstories.com

Scan to contact

www.ingramcontent.com/pod-product-compliance
Lightning Source LLC
LaVergne TN
LVHW071535210926
848349LV00013B/136
9798234103758

SUNNY the SKIN SHIELD

Dedication

To my sons-

You are the reason behind every page, every word, and every dream brought to life in this story. You are my heart, my inspiration, and the reason these stories came to life. Watching you grow, learn, and shine brighter each day is my greatest joy. This book - and the series to come - begins with you and was written with love that will last far beyond these pages.

To every child-

May this story be a reminder that you are strong, bright, and protected. This is just the beginning of a series made to help you grow with confidence, curiosity, and courage wherever life takes you.

Ryu loved to play outside in the warm, sunny air.
He ran, climbed, and laughed all day long.

His big brother, Dash, was always right beside him.
They were the best adventure team.

One morning Ryu said, "Do I have to wear sunscreen?"
He made a little scrunchy face.

Dash laughed and said, "You don't want to get burned!"
"Trust me I've learned the hard way."

That night, Ryu had a dream about his skin.
It looked like a strong, shiny castle.

Suddenly, ZAP! Bright sun rays came zooming down!
"Oh no!" Ryu shouted.

Then a glowing friend appeared.
"I'm Sunny the Shield! I protect your skin!"

Sunny covered the castle like a soft, shiny blanket.
The sun rays bounced right off, BOING!

"They can't get us?" Ryu asked.
"Not if you put sunscreen on every day!" Sunny said.

Ryu woke up with a big smile.
"Dash! We need sunscreen!"

The brothers put sunscreen on their faces, arms, and legs.
"We're protecting our castles!" they cheered.

Now Ryu and Dash wear sunscreen before every adventure.

PARENT PRO TIP
Find a Sunscreen with Zinc Oxide & Titanium Dioxide
ZINC OXIDE
TITANIUM DIOXIDE
HARMFUL UV RAYS
SUNSCREEN LAYER
SKIN SURFACE
SKIN CELLS
DEEPER SKIN LAYERS
They sit on top of the skin and block harmful rays like a tiny shield.
Sunscreen should go on 15 minutes before sun exposure not right as you walk out the door.
Kids need more sunscreen than you think, about a full shot glass amount to cover the whole body.
"Waterproof" sunscreen isn't real. Look for water resistant and always reapply after swimming.
OCT 26
Sunscreen expires! Check the date. Old sunscreen can lose effectiveness.
Sprays are convenient, but lotions protect more evenly. (if using sprays rub them in after applying.)
LIP BALM SPF
Lips burn too – use a lip balm with SPF.
Most parents forget the sun is strongest between 10am-4pm even in cooler weather.
SUNSCREEN SPF 50+
Protecting skin early is one of the easiest ways to prevent long term damage. Little steps now,
BIG PROTECTION FOR LIFE

Pack Your Sun Safety Bag

Draw a line or circle to what belongs in your beach bag.

Sun Safety Word Search

Can you find all the hidden sun safety words?

HAT

SUN

SKIN

SAFE

SUNNY

WATER

SPF

SHADE

Y	U	N	Y	Y	V	O	F	O	G
S	U	N	N	Y	A	S	I	N	E
U	H	A	T	E	R	A	C	S	
N	O	I	D	H	E	F	B	P	
V	S	H	A	D	E	R	F		
W	K	T	T	R	O	H	A		
S	I	I	W	A	T	E	R		
S	N	N	Y	S	S	E	E		

Draw Yourself Having Fun in the Sun!

Can you draw yourself enjoying a sunny day? Don't forget your sun safety gear!

Sun Safety Scavenger Hunt!

Look carefully! Find and circle each item below.

Sun	Shady tree	Hat
Sunglasses	Water bottle	Sunscreen

Color Sunny the Skin Shield!

Help Sunny Get to the Soccer Field

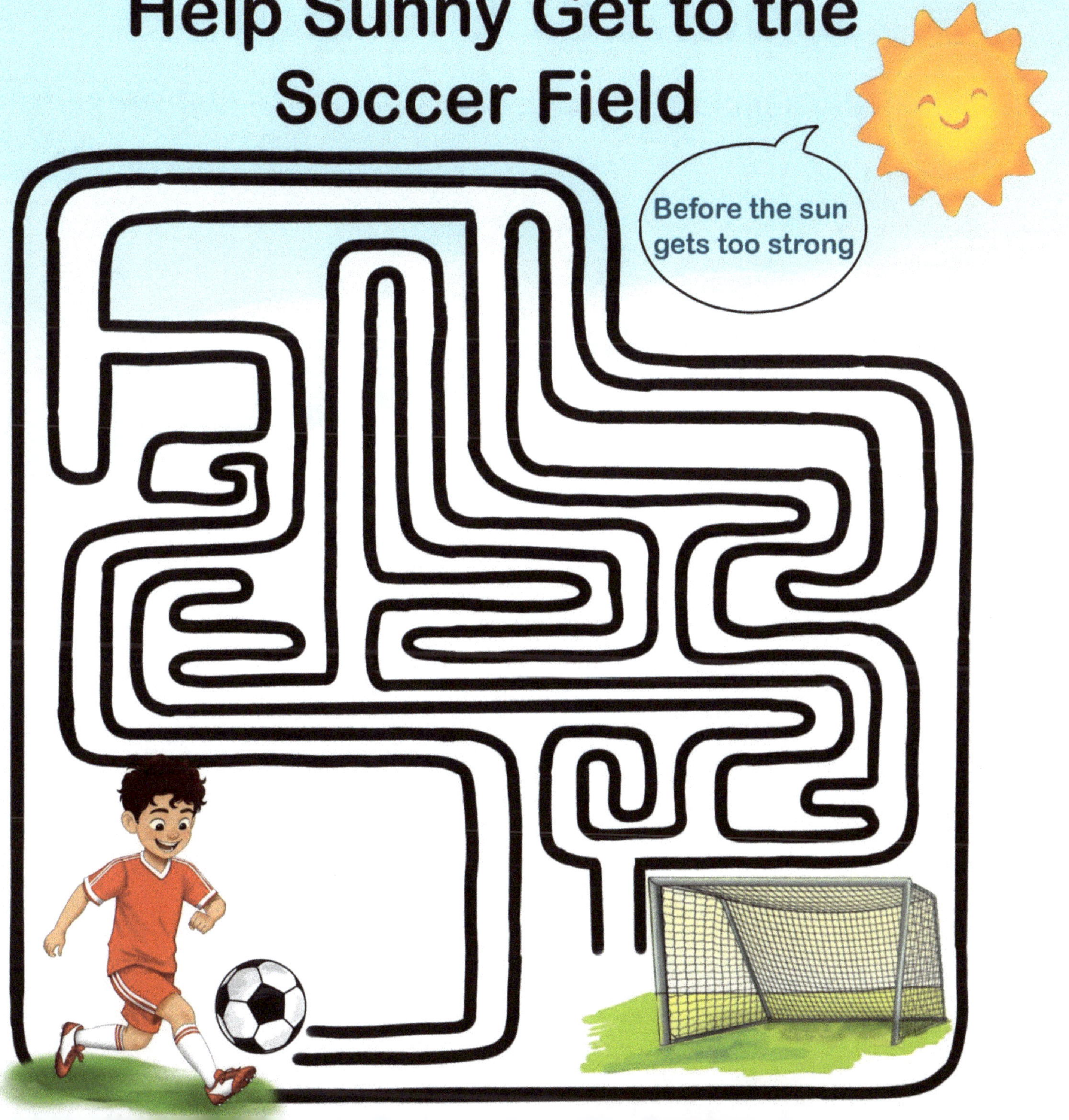

Connect the Dots!

Follow the numbers and discover WHAT THE SURPRISE IS

Match the Colors!

Can you match each color to the correct objects?

Circle the Things That Start with "S"

Can you find everything that begins with the letter S ?

Color by Numbers

Share your sunscreen with your buddy and color the picture with the relevant colors

Sun Safety

Write the correct words on the lines

1. Always wear a ____________  when you are in the sun.

2. ________________ 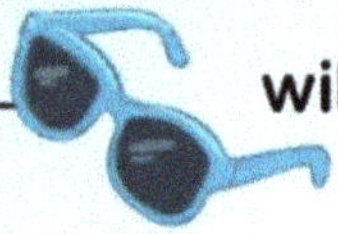 will help to protect your eyes from harmful rays of the sun.

3. Apply plenty of ________________  to protect your skin from harmful rays.

4. After a few ________________ 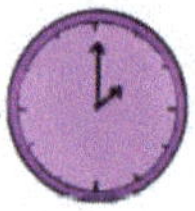 you need to reapply.

5. Cover your skin with a ________________ 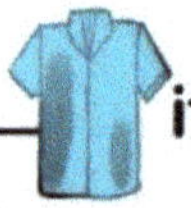 if you can.

6. Play in the ________________  for even better protection from the sun.

shade	hat	hours	sunscreen	shirt	sunglasses

ABOUT THE AUTHOR

Sierra Jeffress is a creative storyteller with a passion for bringing imagination to life through meaningful, engaging narratives. With a background in aesthetics and plastic surgery industry, she blends science, care, and creativity into everything she does.

Inspired by her love for children and storytelling, Sierra writes books that spark curiosity, build confidence, and make learning fun. Her work focuses on turning everyday lessons - like sun safety - into magical, memorable adventures.

When she's not writing, Sierra enjoys spending time with her family, working in the world of advanced skincare and laser treatments, and creating content that educates and inspires others.

ABOUT THE ILLUSTRATOR

Farheen Fatima is a Canadian children's book illustrator who brings warmth, imagination, and charm to every page she creates. With a playful illustration style and a keen eye for detail, she transforms stories into engaging visual experiences that captivate young readers.

Passionate about visual storytelling, Farheen loves collaborating with authors and publishers to bring new tales to life through her artwork.

Ready to bring your story to life? Get in touch to discuss your project and create something children will treasure for years to come.

www.littlefolkstories.com

design@littlefolkstories.com

Scan to contact

www.ingramcontent.com/pod-product-compliance
Lightning Source LLC
LaVergne TN
LVHW071535210926
848349LV00013B/136

DEDICATION

To my sons-
You are the reason behind every page, every word, and every dream brought to life in this story. You are my heart, my inspiration, and the reason these stories came to life. Watching you grow, learn, and shine brighter each day is my greatest joy. This book - and the series to come - begins with you and was written with love that will last far beyond these pages.

To every child-
May this story be a reminder that you are strong, bright, and protected. This is just the beginning of a series made to help you grow with confidence, curiosity, and courage wherever life takes you.

Ryu loved to play outside in the warm, sunny air.
He ran, climbed, and laughed all day long.

His big brother, Dash, was always right beside him.
They were the best adventure team.

One morning Ryu said, "Do I have to wear sunscreen?"
He made a little scrunchy face.

Dash laughed and said, "You don't want to get burned!"
"Trust me I've learned the hard way."

That night, Ryu had a dream about his skin.
It looked like a strong, shiny castle.

Suddenly, ZAP! Bright sun rays came zooming down!
"Oh no!" Ryu shouted.

Then a glowing friend appeared.
"I'm Sunny the Shield! I protect your skin!"

Sunny covered the castle like a soft, shiny blanket.
The sun rays bounced right off, BOING!

"They can't get us?" Ryu asked.
"Not if you put sunscreen on every day!" Sunny said.

Ryu woke up with a big smile.
"Dash! We need sunscreen!"

The brothers put sunscreen on their faces, arms, and legs. "We're protecting our castles!" they cheered.

Now Ryu and Dash wear sunscreen before every adventure.

PARENT PRO TIP

Find a Sunscreen with Zinc Oxide & Titanium Dioxide

- Sunscreen should go on 15 minutes before sun exposure not right as you walk out the door.
- Kids need more sunscreen than you think, about a full shot glass amount to cover the whole body.
- "Waterproof" sunscreen isn't real. Look for water resistant and always reapply after swimming.
- Sunscreen expires! Check the date. Old sunscreen can lose effectiveness.
- Sprays are convenient, but lotions protect more evenly. (If using sprays rub them in after applying.)
- Lips burn too – use a lip balm with SPF.
- Most parents forget the sun is strongest between 10am-4pm even in cooler weather.

Protecting skin early is one of the easiest ways to prevent long term damage. Little steps now,

BIG PROTECTION FOR LIFE

Pack Your Sun Safety Bag

Draw a line or circle to what belongs in your beach bag.

Sun Safety Word Search

Can you find all the hidden sun safety words?

- SUN
- SKIN
- SUNNY
- SPF
- HAT
- SAFE
- WATER
- SHADE

Y	U	N	Y	Y	V	O	F	O	G
S	U	N	N	Y	A	S	I	N	E
U	H	A	T	E	R	A	C	S	
N	O	I	D	H	E	F	B	P	
V	S	H	A	D	E	R	F		
W	K	T	T	R	O	H	A		
S	I	I	W	A	T	E	R		
S	N	N	Y	S	S	E	E		

Draw Yourself Having Fun in the Sun!

Can you draw yourself enjoying a sunny day?
Don't forget your sun safety gear!

Sun Safety Scavenger Hunt!

Look carefully! Find and circle each item below.

Sun	Shady tree	Hat
Sunglasses	Water bottle	Sunscreen

Color Sunny the Skin Shield!

Help Sunny Get to the Soccer Field

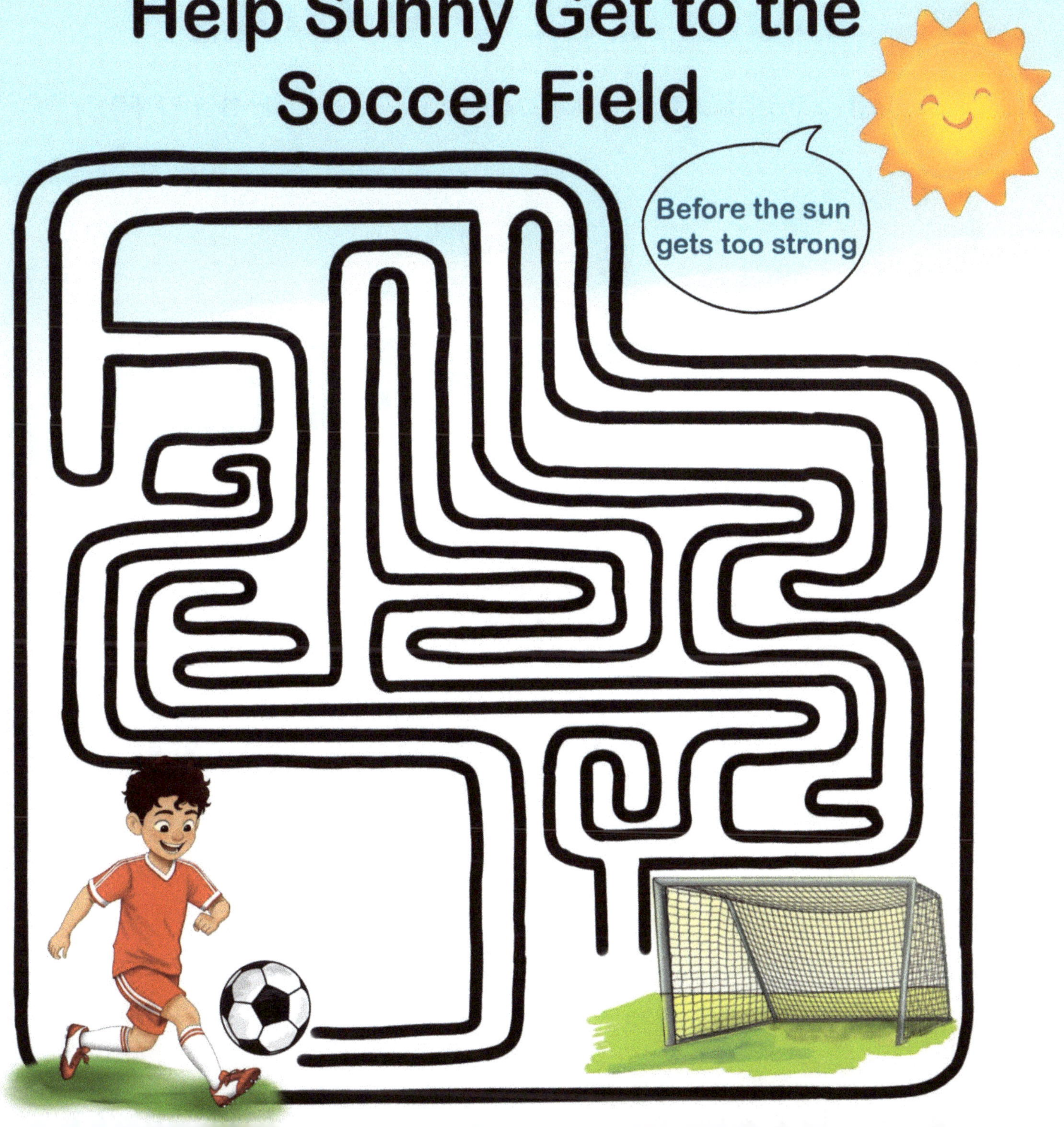

Connect the Dots!

Follow the numbers and discover WHAT THE SURPRISE IS

Match the Colors!

Can you match each color to the correct objects?

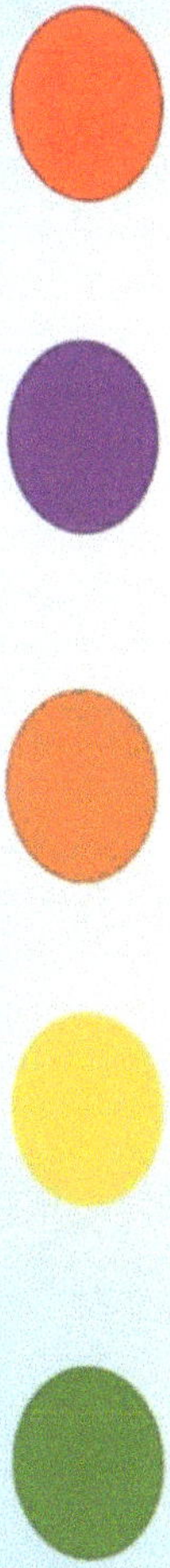

Circle the Things That Start with "S"

Can you find everything that begins with the letter S ?

Color by Numbers

Share your sunscreen with your buddy and color the picture with the relevant colors

1 2 3 4 5 6 7 8 9

Sun Safety

Write the correct words on the lines

1. Always wear a ____________  when you are in the sun.

2. ________________ 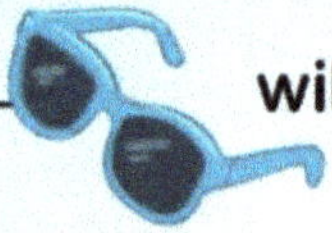 will help to protect your eyes from harmful rays of the sun.

3. Apply plenty of ______________ 

to protect your skin from harmful rays.

4. After a few ______________ 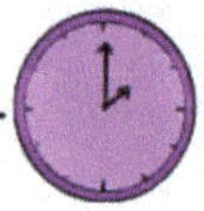 you need to reapply.

5. Cover your skin with a ______________  if you can.

6. Play in the ______________  for even better protection from the sun.

shade	hat	hours	sunscreen	shirt	sunglasses

ABOUT THE AUTHOR

Sierra Jeffress is a creative storyteller with a passion for bringing imagination to life through meaningful, engaging narratives. With a background in aesthetics and plastic surgery industry, she blends science, care, and creativity into everything she does.

Inspired by her love for children and storytelling, Sierra writes books that spark curiosity, build confidence, and make learning fun. Her work focuses on turning everyday lessons - like sun safety - into magical, memorable adventures.

When she's not writing, Sierra enjoys spending time with her family, working in the world of advanced skincare and laser treatments, and creating content that educates and inspires others.

ABOUT THE ILLUSTRATOR

Farheen Fatima is a Canadian children's book illustrator who brings warmth, imagination, and charm to every page she creates. With a playful illustration style and a keen eye for detail, she transforms stories into engaging visual experiences that captivate young readers.

Passionate about visual storytelling, Farheen loves collaborating with authors and publishers to bring new tales to life through her artwork.

Ready to bring your story to life? Get in touch to discuss your project and create something children will treasure for years to come.

www.littlefolkstories.com

design@littlefolkstories.com

Scan to contact

DEDICATION

To my sons–
You are the reason behind every page, every word, and every dream brought to life in this story. You are my heart, my inspiration, and the reason these stories came to life. Watching you grow, learn, and shine brighter each day is my greatest joy. This book - and the series to come - begins with you and was written with love that will last far beyond these pages.

To every child–
May this story be a reminder that you are strong, bright, and protected. This is just the beginning of a series made to help you grow with confidence, curiosity, and courage wherever life takes you.

Ryu loved to play outside in the warm, sunny air.
He ran, climbed, and laughed all day long.

His big brother, Dash, was always right beside him.
They were the best adventure team.

One morning Ryu said, "Do I have to wear sunscreen?"
He made a little scrunchy face.

Dash laughed and said, "You don't want to get burned!"
"Trust me I've learned the hard way."

That night, Ryu had a dream about his skin.
It looked like a strong, shiny castle.

Suddenly, ZAP! Bright sun rays came zooming down!
"Oh no!" Ryu shouted.

Then a glowing friend appeared.
"I'm Sunny the Shield! I protect your skin!"

Sunny covered the castle like a soft, shiny blanket.
The sun rays bounced right off, BOING!

"They can't get us?" Ryu asked.
"Not if you put sunscreen on every day!" Sunny said.

Ryu woke up with a big smile.
"Dash! We need sunscreen!"

The brothers put sunscreen on their faces, arms, and legs. "We're protecting our castles!" they cheered.

Now Ryu and Dash wear sunscreen before every adventure.

PARENT PRO TIP
Find a Sunscreen with
Zinc Oxide & Titanium Dioxide
ZINC OXIDE
TITANIUM DIOXIDE
HARMFUL UV RAYS
SUNSCREEN LAYER
SKIN SURFACE
SKIN CELLS
DEEPER SKIN LAYERS
They sit on top of the skin and block harmful rays like a tiny shield.
Sunscreen should go on 15 minutes before sun exposure not right as you walk out the door.
Kids need more sunscreen than you think, about a full shot glass amount to cover the whole body.
"Waterproof" sunscreen isn't real. Look for water resistant and always reapply after swimming.
OCT 26
Sunscreen expires! Check the date. Old sunscreen can lose effectiveness.
Sprays are convenient, but lotions protect more evenly. (If using sprays rub them in after applying.)
LIP BALM SPF
Lips burn too – use a lip balm with SPF.
Most parents forget the sun is strongest between 10am-4pm even in cooler weather.
SUNSCREEN SPF 50+
Protecting skin early is one of the easiest ways to prevent long term damage. Little steps now,
BIG PROTECTION FOR LIFE

Pack Your Sun Safety Bag

Draw a line or circle to what belongs in your beach bag.

Sun Safety Word Search

Can you find all the hidden sun safety words?

HAT

SUN

SKIN

SAFE

SUNNY

WATER

SPF

SHADE

Y U N Y Y V O F O G
S U N N Y A S I N E
U H A T E R A C S
N O I D H E F B P
V S H A D E R F
W K T T R O H A
S I I W A T E R
S N N Y S S E E

Draw Yourself Having Fun in the Sun!

Can you draw yourself enjoying a sunny day?
Don't forget your sun safety gear!

Sun Safety Scavenger Hunt!

Look carefully! Find and circle each item below.

Sun	Shady tree	Hat
Sunglasses	Water bottle	Sunscreen

Color Sunny the Skin Shield!

Help Sunny Get to the Soccer Field

Connect the Dots!

Follow the numbers and discover WHAT THE SURPRISE IS

Match the Colors!

Can you match each color to the correct objects?

Circle the Things That Start with "S"

Can you find everything that begins with the letter S ?

Color by Numbers

Share your sunscreen with your buddy and color the picture with the relevant colors

Sun Safety

Write the correct words on the lines

1. Always wear a __________  when you are in the sun.

2. ______________ 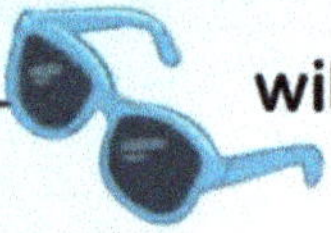 will help to protect your eyes from harmful rays of the sun.

3. Apply plenty of ______________ 

to protect your skin from harmful rays.

4. After a few ______________  you need to reapply.

5. Cover your skin with a ______________ 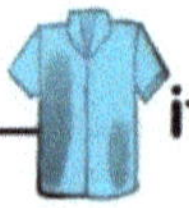 if you can.

6. Play in the ______________  for even better protection from the sun.

shade	hat	hours	sunscreen	shirt	sunglasses

ABOUT THE AUTHOR

Sierra Jeffress is a creative storyteller with a passion for bringing imagination to life through meaningful, engaging narratives. With a background in aesthetics and plastic surgery industry, she blends science, care, and creativity into everything she does.

Inspired by her love for children and storytelling, Sierra writes books that spark curiosity, build confidence, and make learning fun. Her work focuses on turning everyday lessons - like sun safety - into magical, memorable adventures.

When she's not writing, Sierra enjoys spending time with her family, working in the world of advanced skincare and laser treatments, and creating content that educates and inspires others.

ABOUT THE ILLUSTRATOR

Farheen Fatima is a Canadian children's book illustrator who brings warmth, imagination, and charm to every page she creates. With a playful illustration style and a keen eye for detail, she transforms stories into engaging visual experiences that captivate young readers.

Passionate about visual storytelling, Farheen loves collaborating with authors and publishers to bring new tales to life through her artwork.

Ready to bring your story to life? Get in touch to discuss your project and create something children will treasure for years to come.

www.littlefolkstories.com

design@littlefolkstories.com

Scan to contact

www.ingramcontent.com/pod-product-compliance
Lightning Source LLC
LaVergne TN
LVHW071535210926
848349LV00013B/136
9798234103758